# THE ECOLOGY OF
# WASTE WATER TREATMENT

# THE ECOLOGY OF WASTE WATER TREATMENT

*by*

## H. A. HAWKES

*Department of Biology*
*College of Advanced Technology*
*Birmingham*

PERGAMON PRESS

OXFORD · LONDON · NEW YORK · PARIS

1963

PERGAMON PRESS LTD
*Headington Hill Hall, Oxford*
*4 and 5 Fitzroy Square, London, W. 1*

PERGAMON PRESS INC.
*122 East 55th Street, New York 22, N.Y.*

GAUTHIER-VILLARS ED.
*55 Quai des Grands-Augustins, Paris, 6ᵉ*

PERGAMON PRESS G.m.b.H.
*75 Kaiserstrasse, Frankfurt am Main*


Distributed in the Western Hemisphere by
THE MACMILLAN COMPANY · NEW YORK
pursuant to a special arrangement with
Pergamon Press Limited

Library of Congress Catalogue Card Number 62-16424

Printed in Hungary

# CONTENTS

# PREFACE

THE treatment of waste waters, both domestic sewage and industrial effluents, usually depends, at some stage of the process, upon the activity of living organisms. Biological oxidation plants such as bacteria beds (unfortunately also termed "filters") and activated sludge plants are designed and operated by engineers and chemists who, in many cases, have little or no biological training. Such workers often find themselves in charge of the design, construction or operation of biological oxidation plants and not fully equipped to create a suitable environment for, or control the activity of, the myriads of "workers" employed in the processes of purification. Furthermore, the invasion of the plant by trouble-causing organisms presents another biological problem. The aim of waste water treatment is the prevention of river pollution; in assessing the effect of a discharge on the receiving water, a knowledge of the biological as well as the chemical and physical effects is desirable.

The treatment of waste waters in biological oxidation plants may be regarded as the environmental control of the activity of populations of the necessary organisms. Ecology, the theme of this book, is that branch of biological study which deals with the inter-relationships of populations and their environment. Any team working on waste water treatment problems, involving biological oxidation, should include a biologist. Even when this *is* the case the utmost co-operation is needed between the different professions involved, and without some understanding of the biology of the process, the non-biologist may have difficulty in appreciating the biologist's contribution. The aim of this book is to provide some understanding of the biological aspects of waste water treatment for the non-biologist employed in this field. The recommendation of a suitable introductory text book on biology for this purpose has been found difficult. Most "introductions to biology" would involve the reader in such studies as "the cranial nerves of the dogfish" or "the pollination mechanism of the sweet-pea" with little or no reference to those groups of organisms he would find in his treatment plant nor to the biological principles involved. The many ramifications of ecology fringe on other branches of the biological sciences, such as taxonomy, physiology and biochemistry, and it is difficult to clearly limit the scope of the subject. The more advanced text books which deal with these subjects, some of which are referred to in the text, assume the reader has a basic biological training and furthermore because of the specialized nature of our subject it is necessary to refer to several such books to cover the different aspects involved. In an attempt to meet this need the first chapter deals with those basic principles of biology considered necessary for an understanding of the following sections in which the dominant organisms present in different waste water treatment processes, are first enumerated and then the factors influencing their numbers and activity are considered, and finally the practical application of these factors to plant design and operation is discussed.

Chapters 1 and 3 are based on a paper "Ecology of activated sludge and bacteria beds" which was presented by kind permission of Mr. M.R.Vincent Daviss, B. Sc., M.I.C.E., Engineer to the Birmingham Tame and Rea District Drainage Board, at the Second Symposium on the Treatment of Waste Waters, organized by Mr. P. C. G. Isaac, at the University of Durham, in September 1959, the proceedings of which were published as *"Waste Treatment"* (Pergamon Press, Oxford 1960).

Mr. Isaac suggested that the original paper could well be expanded to form a separate publication. The present book is the outcome of that suggestion which I gratefully acknowledge. The work is an attempted synthesis of the results of workers in many parts of the world. The synthesis of sometimes conflicting results and views has not been easy but it is hoped that a generally balanced view of our present state of knowledge has been presented. Again, the dangers of generalization and over-simplification of the theoretical aspects discussed in the different sections, is fully appreciated. However, it was considered that if each statement were qualified by a list of exceptions and if each topic were discussed in detail, the more important practical aspects would be obscured.

Chapters 3, 6 and 7 contain the results of my own investigations on the ecology of bacteria beds. I wish to express my thanks to Dr.

Ll. Lloyd, formerly of Leeds University, who first interested me in this subject and to him and to Dr. S. H. Jenkins, Board's Chemist, for their continued encouragement and interest in my work. To all who have assisted me and to many former colleagues on the Board's staff both in the laboratory, in the drawing offices and on the works who have influenced my thinking, I express my gratitude. Acknowledgements are given individually in respect of the several diagrams which have been reproduced.

I fully appreciate the inadequacy of discussing organisms the names of which do not create a visual impression in the mind of the reader. For this reason I have prepared the somewhat diagrammatic drawings representative of the range of organisms discussed, which do not form part of the common experience of the average person. *Figures,* 1.1–1.5 are intended for this purpose and not for use in identification, for which purpose much more detailed drawings are required.

It is sincerely hoped that the following chapters will contribute to a fuller understanding by the non-biologist of the biological aspects of waste water treatment and thus enable a closer co-operation of engineer, chemist and biologist, in their joint task of creating more wholesome environments in our streams and rivers.

*Birmingham*                                                    H. A. H.

# CHAPTER 1

# AN INTRODUCTION
# TO THE RELEVANT ASPECTS
# OF BIOLOGY

OF the many branches of biology, we need concern ourselves chiefly with the naming and classification of organisms—Taxonomy, their activities or functioning—Physiology, and their inter-relationships with the environment—Ecology.

## TAXONOMY

To the non-biologist, the naming and classification of organisms is the most difficult aspect of biology and to many it is probably a deterrent to further study of the subject. A universal system of scientific nomenclature is essential for the interchange of information on organisms and the specific identification of organisms is desirable. Nevertheless the identification of species in many groups is a task for the specialist on that group of organisms and is often outside the scope of the general biologist, let alone the chemist or engineer!

With experience, however, it is possible to become acquainted with the more commonly occurring species in plants, the numbers of species being limited by the specialized nature of the habitat. The inability to name the species present in a plant should not, however, prevent one understanding the factors influencing their different activities in the process of treatment.

It is usual to refer to organisms by two names, firstly the generic name denoting the genus and secondly the specific name by which it is distinguished from other species of the genus. In script it is conventional to underline generic and specific names and in print they appear

1

in italics. Thus the common bacteria bed fly is *Psychoda alternata* and its less frequently occurring relative, *Psychoda severini*. In cases where specific identification is not possible it is usual to refer to the generic name only—*Psychoda* sp. or *Psychoda* spp. if referring to more than one species. Different species cannot interbreed to produce fertile offspring but may differ only in some small detail of structure. Such closely related species are grouped together into a genus, and similar genera into families and then through orders, classes, phyla into kingdoms, each grouping thus successively containing a greater diversity of organisms. The classification of organisms is based on structure and is in no way ecological. Thus species of the same genus may occupy entirely different ecological niches, which they share with species from widely different genera. It would appear that in evolution the different species of a genus have radiated to fill different available niches. The many forms of life inhabiting the earth today are considered to have been evolved from common stock and represent the more successful lines of evolution, many of the ancestral stock and less successful lines having died out. Although this selective elimination has left us with fairly well defined groups of organisms, making classification possible, the grouping is necessarily arbitrary and it is not surprising, therefore, that different classifications are found. Although not conventional, it is for our purpose convenient, to recognize three kingdoms of living organisms, plant, animal and a third kingdom which includes the fungi and bacteria. The major phyla in these kingdoms are given in *Table* 1.1, the phyla of particular interest in our present study being indicated by capitals. *Table* 1.2 shows the further division of these phyla with examples of the systematic position of some commonly occurring organisms.

Structurally and functionally the basic unit of most organisms is the cell which is usually of microscopic size. This term was first applied to plant tissues where the cells are separated by a cellulose wall which is not found in animal tissues. Cells may be defined as unit masses of protoplasm contained within a limiting membrane and, in the case of plants, within a more rigid cell wall. Protoplasm may be regarded as a colloidal solution of proteins, lipoids and other substances which together possess the properties of life. The protoplasm of a cell is differentiated into cytoplasm, the outermost portion of which forms the limiting membrane—the cytoplasmic membrane, and a more

TABLE 1.1. THE MAJOR PHYLA OF THE THREE KINGDOMS OF LIVING ORGANISMS
[The phyla containing organisms of importance in waste water treatment
are given in capitals]

| Kingdom | Phylum | | |
|---|---|---|---|
| PLANT | | | |
| | THALLOPHYTA | — | Primitive plants with little or no differentiation of thallus |
| | Bryophyta | — | Mosses and Liverworts |
| | Pteridophyta | — | Ferns and Horsetails |
| | Spermaphyta | — | Seed-bearing plants |
| FUNGI AND BACTERIA | | | |
| | FUNGI | | |
| | BACTERIA | | |
| | Viruses | | |
| ANIMAL | PROTOZOA | — | Non-cellular microscopic animals |
| | Porifera | — | Sponges |
| | Coelenterata | — | Simple animals having 2 layered body wall enclosing single body cavity e.g. *Hydra*, Jellyfishes |
| | PLATYHELMINTHES | — | Flatworms |
| | NEMATODA | — | Unsegmented roundworms |
| | ROTIFERA | — | Wheel animalcules |
| | Polyzoa | — | Moss animals |
| | ANNELIDA | — | True segmented worms |
| | ARTHROPODA | — | Animals with exo-skeleton and several many jointed limbs |
| | Mollusca | — | Snails, Limpets, Cockles and Mussels |
| | Chordata | — | Mostly possessing backbones |

(Invertebrates) — (Vertebrates)

Metazoa

TABLE 1.2. THE FURTHER DIVISION OF PHYLA INTO CLASSES ETC. SHOWING THE SYSTEMATIC POSITION OF SOME ORGANISMS OF IMPORTANCE IN WASTE WATER TREATMENT

**Phylum**
    SUB-PHYLUM
      CLASS
        SUB-CLASS
          *Order*

THALLOPHYTA
  ALGAE
    CYANOPHYCEAE  —  *Phormidium, Oscillatoria*
    (BLUE-GREEN
    ALGAE)
    BACILLARIACEAE — Single celled siliceous frustules, *Cocconeis.*
    (DIATOMS)
    CHLOROPHYCEAE — Contain the pigment chlorophyll.
    (GREEN
    ALGAE)

| | |
|---|---|
| *Volvocales* | — Unicellular or colonial. *Chlamydomonas, Gonium.* |
| *Chlorococcales* | — Unicellular or colonial, vegetative cells non-motile. *Scenedesmus.* |
| *Ulothrichales* | — Septate filaments, plates or tubes. *Ulothrix. Enteromorpha, Monostroma.* |
| *Cladophorales* | — Filaments usually branched, cells multi-nucleate *Cladophora* (Blanketweed) |
| *Chaetophorales* | — Filaments with prostrate and projecting systems. *Stigeoclonium.* |
| *Oedogoniales* | — Filamentous, ends of cells striated. *Oedogonium.* |
| *Conjugales* | — Elaborate chloroplasts, no motile spores. |
| | Zygnemaceae — Filamentous. *Spirogyra.* |
| | Desmidiaceae — Mostly unicellular. *Closterium.* |
| *Siphonales* | — Filaments non-septate. *Vaucheria.* |

    RHODOPHYCEAE  — Elaboration of thallus. *Batrachospermum.*
    (RED ALGAE)

  BACTERIA
    BACTERIA      — (Schizomycetes — fission-fungi)

*Eubacteriales:* Mostly flagellate and unicellular.
    Spirillaceae: Markedly spiral; flagella polar. *Spirillum.*
    Pseudomonadaceae: Rod-shaped with long polar flagella. *Nitrosomonas, Pseudomonas.*
    Bacteriaceae: Non-sporing rod-shaped forms. *Bacterium coli, Shigella, Salmonella.*
    Chlamydobacteriaceae: Bacterium-like with mucous sheaths or stalks, and flagellated swarmers. *Sphaerotilus.*
    Bacillaceae: Rod-shaped with endospores. *Bacillus Clostridium.*
    Coccaceae: Radially symmetrical, usually non-motile. *Staphylococcus.*
*Actinomycetales:* Filaments with impermanent branches.
    Mycobacteriaceae: Short filaments. *Mycobacterium.*

FUNGI

PHYCOMYCETES — Non-septate filaments. *Leptomitus, Saprolegnia.*
FUNGI — Life cycle not fully known. *Fusarium, Geotrichum.*
IMPERFECTI *Sepedonium.*

PROTOZOA

RHIZOPODA
    AMOEBINA — Move and ingest food by pseudopodia.
        *Nuda* — without shells. *Amoeba.*
        *Testacea* — with shells. *Arcella, Difflugia.*
  FLAGELLATA. (MASTIGOPHORA) — Move by whip-like flagella
    PHYTOMASTIGINA — Plant-like having pigments.
        *Euglenoidina* — spindle-shaped with 1 flagellum. *Euglena.*
    ZOOMASTIGINA — Have no pigment and usually 2 or more flagella. *Bodo.*
  CILIOPHORA — Move by hair-like cilia.
    CILIATA — Ciliated throughout life.
        *Holotricha* — Uniformly ciliated. *Paramoecium.*
        *Heterotricha* — Fine cilia with stouter cilia arranged in bands. *Stentor.*
        *Hypotricha* — Flattened ciliates having stiffer cilia ventrally as legs. *Aspidisca, Stylonychia, Euplotes.*
        *Peritricha* — Bell-shaped bodies borne on stalks. *Vorticella, Opercularia, Carchesium, Epistylis.*
  SUCTORIA — Only ciliated in larval stage, have suctorial tentacles in adults. *Acineta, Podophrya.*

PLATYHELMINTHES

TURBELLARIA — Free-living flat worms. *Planaria, Dendrocoelum.*
TREMATODA — Parasitic, Flukes. *Bilharzia.*
CESTODA — Parasitic, Tapeworms. *Taenia.*

NEMATODA — Free-living terrestrial or aquatic. *Rhabditis. Nematoda.*
— Parasitic. *Ascaris, Enterobius.*

ROTIFERA — Several orders, most important being

        *Bdelloida* — which are capable of swimming by ciliated discs and creep by looping movements as do leeches, forked telescopic tail. *Philodina, Rotifer.*

ANNELIDA

OLIGOCHAETA — The earthworms and allies having chaetae or bristles.
    *Terricolae* — mostly terrestrial.
        Lumbricidae — Large earthworms. *Lumbricus, Eisenia.*

*Limicolae* — aquatic, usually smaller.

Tubificidae — Usually above 3 cm long with red blood, more than 2 chaetae per bundle, ventral ones cleft a. tips. *Tubifex.*

Enchytraeidae — Less than 3·5 cm long, more than 2 chaetae per bundle, simple pointed. *Lumbricillus, Enchytraeus*

Lumbriculidae — Up to 8 cm long with dark ted blood, 2 chaetae per bundle, Simple or cleft. *Lumbriculus.*

Naididae — Up to 20 mm long, often in chains of several individuals, chaetae of ventral bundles with cleft tips. *Nais, Chaetogaster.*

Aelosomatidae — Less than 10 mm long with long hairlike chaetae in both dorsal bundles. Integument containing pigmented bodies. *Aelosoma.*

HIRUDINEA — Leeches, no chaeta but have suckers. *Erpobdella, Glosssiphonia.*

ARTHROPODA

CRUSTACEA — Aquatic with 2 pairs antennae, at least 3 pairs appendages acting as jaws.

*Entomostraca.* {

**Branchiopoda** — Trunk limbs broadly lobed and fringed with hairs *Daphnia* (Water Flea)

**Ostracoda** — Body enclosed in bi-valved carapace. *Cypris.*

**Copepoda** — No carapace, antennae large. *Cyclops.*

**Malacostraca** — 8 thoracic and 6 abdominal segments all with appendages

*Isopoda* — Carapace absent, body flattened dorsoventrally *Asellus* (Water Hog Louse).

*Amphipoda* — Carapace absent, body flattened laterally. *Gammarus.* (Freshwater Shrimp)

*Decapoda* — Possessing 5 pairs of thoracic walking limbs. *Astacus.* (Crayfish)

INSECTA — Body of adult divided into head, thorax and abdomen, normally with 2 pairs of wings and 3 pairs of walking legs on thorax.

**Apterygota** — Without wings.

*Collembola* — Abdomen having 6 segments. *Achorutes. Tomocerus, Folsomia.*

**Pterygota** — With wings.

**(I) Exopterygota** — Wings developing externally, shortened life cycle.

*Plecoptera* — Stone-flies. *Perla.*
*Ephemeroptera* — May-flies. *Baetis, Ephemera.*
*Odonata* — Dragon-flies. *Aeschna*
*Hemiptera* — Bugs. *Corixa* (Water Boatman), *Velia* (Water Cricket).

**(II) Endopterygota** — Wings developing internally, full life cycle.

*Neuroptera* — Alder-flies. *Sialis*.
*Trichoptera* — Caddis-flies. *Hydropsyche*.
*Coleoptera* — Beetles. *Cercyon*.
*Diptera* — 2-winged flies. *Anisopus, Psychoda*.

ARACHNIDA — Lack sensory antennae, possess 4 pairs walking limbs.

*Araneida* — Spiders, body divided into 2 by narrow waist. abdomen unsegmented.
*Acarina* — Body rounded not divided. Mites.

*Platyseius.*

*(Tardigrad )* — Bear animalcules, 4 pairs of stumpy legs.

MOLLUSCA

GASTROPODA — Snails and limpets having shell in one piece. *Lymnaea, Planorbis*.

LAMELLIBRANCHIATA — Mussels and cockles, shells having 2 valves. *Sphaerium, Anadonta*.

specialized body—the nucleus—which governs the activity of the cytoplasm. The cytoplasm may also contain other granules and vacuoles or cavities containing food reserves (*Fig.* 1.1). The cell membranes are not only of importance structurally in determining the shape of the cell but are functionally important in that they act as selective permeable membranes which, as we shall see, are important in maintaining the water content of cells and in the selective absorption of suitable food material.

The nucleus contains a specific number of thread-like structures—the chromosomes—the number and shape of which are characteristic of the species, a feature which can be used in specific identification. On the chromosomes are carried the genes which may be regarded as the hereditary blue-prints for the species. Growth or multiplication occurs by the division of one cell into two followed by the increase in size of each daughter cell. This division is preceded by a complicated division of the nucleus in which each chromosome splits lengthways, one half of each passing into the resultant daughter nuclei, thus ensuring a similar genetic constitution in the two daughter cells. The chromosomes, which are only evident at times of cell division, occur in pairs of similar shape and size, one of each pair being contributed by each parent. In the production of sex cells (gametes), the chromosome numbers are halved, one from each pair passing to each daughter nucleus in the two resultant cells. Thus, when the gametes from the

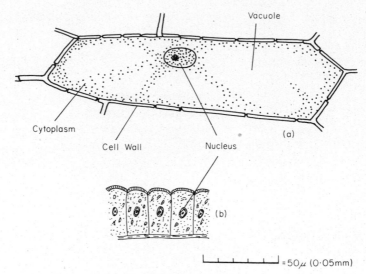

FIG. 1.1.  Examples of plant and animal cells.
(a)  Cells forming the epidermal skin of onion.
(b)  Cells from epithelial lining of gut wall.

two parents fuse (fertilization), the normal chromosome number is again re-established in the resultant cell (the zygote). Furthermore the segregation of the paired chromosomes in the parents and the chance regrouping, provides the possibility of infinite variation in the character of the offspring within the general plan of the species. In the case of multicellular organisms the fertilized egg, by a succession of divisions, gives rise to a new individual, the cells becoming differentially modified for their several functions.

## PLANT KINGDOM

### Phylum Thallophyta

This is the most primitive of the four phyla into which the plant kingdom is divided. Plants of this phylum show no differentiation into root, stem and leaves as do higher forms, their vegetative structure is known as a thallus. Botanists include both algae and fungi in this phylum, but as mentioned above we shall consider the fungi along with bacteria as a third kingdom separated from both animals and plants.

*Algae*

Algae are a diverse group of primitive plants which contain pigments, the possession of which, in common with other plants as opposed to animals, enables them to synthesize their own food material from carbon dioxide and water in the presence of light. The pigment may be diffused throughout the cytoplasm but more often is concentrated in special bodies—the chloroplasts. The shapes of the chloroplasts are sometimes a diagnostic feature of the species. Some algae, e.g. *Chlamydomonas* (*Fig.* 1.2a) are one-celled and of microscopic size; they are free swimming and when present in sufficient numbers impart a green colour to the water. Other algae may, in their life cycles, form similar one-celled stages although one order (Conjugales) which includes the filamentous forms such as *Spirogyra* (*Fig.* 1.2b) and the beautiful bilaterally symmetrical Desmids (*Fig.* 1.2c), is characterized by the absence of motile reproductive cells. Elaboration of the single celled type has resulted in colonial forms of definite numbers in rows e.g. *Scenedesmus* (*Fig.* 1.2d), plates, e.g. *Pediastrum* (*Fig.* 1.2e) or spheres e.g. *Gonium*. A more common line of evolution, however, has given rows of cells of indefinite length producing filamentous growths either unbranched e.g. *Ulothrix* (*Fig.* 1.2f) or branched e.g. *Stigeoclonium* (*Fig.* 2.1d). Further elaboration has led to flat or tubular ribbons (e.g. *Monostroma*, *Enteromorpha*) similar to the marine algae—the seaweeds. The classification of the algae is based largely on the type of pigment they contain. Three classes are represented in biological treatment plants.

*Class Cyanophyceae* (Myxophyceae) (blue-green algae). This is a well defined class, the members differing markedly from other algae in possessing a blue-green pigmentation, their production of mucilage, often in the form of sheaths, and the absence of well defined reproductive cells. Some—the Oscillatoriaceae—exhibit gliding or oscillating movements; of these *Phormidium* (*Fig.* 2.1c) is of common occurrence on the surface of bacteria beds, where it may form thick olive-green sheets of growth preventing the free passage of the liquid into the bed. These sheets are formed from the coalescence of the adjacent sheaths of the filaments.

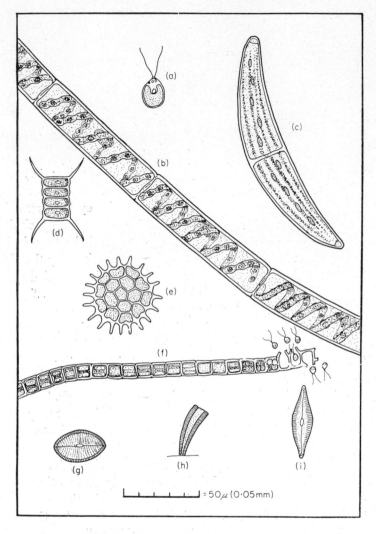

Fig. 1.2.    Some different forms of Algae.

(a)    *Chlamydomonas.*
(b)    *Spirogyra.*
(c)    *Closterium* — (a Desmid)
(d)    *Scenedesmus*
(e)    *Pediastrum*

(f)    *Ulothrix*      ⎫
(g)    *Cocconeis*    ⎪
(h)    *Rhoicosphenia* ⎬ Diatoms
(i)    *Navicula*      ⎭

*Class Chlorophyceae*—(green algae) Here, the members contain the pigment chlorophyll identical with that found in higher plants. These are the most common fresh-water class of algae and are represented in waste treatment plants by unicellular forms which may be free swimming in the liquid or form ill-defined colonies on surfaces Thicker growths are produced on the surface of bacteria beds by fila. mentous forms such as *Ulothrix* or *Stigeoclonium*. The foliaceous *Monostroma* may form concentric rings of growth between the jet lines on circular beds with rotating distributors.

*Class Bacillariaceae* (diatoms) These organisms are unicellular although sometimes aggregated into colonies. They are characterized by possessing cell walls of silica—known as frustules—which are composed of two distinct halves, the one half fitting over the other in the manner of lid and box. Diatoms are usually brown and the frustules are beautifully sculptured; the shape and sculpturing of the frustules are the basis of classification. (*Fig.* 1.2g–i).

*Phylum Bryophyta*

This phylum includes the mosses and liverworts, both moisture loving groups. Although primitive, they show an advance on the algae in the greater elaboration of the thallus and the possession of characteristic sex organs; reproduction, however, as in the algae is by means of spores as opposed to the seeds of higher plants. The liverworts form flat lobed sheet-like growths in moist habitats such as on the surface of bacteria beds e.g. *Marchantia*. The better known mosses which usually have well defined leaves arranged spirally on a stem are also a common feature of the surface growths of some beds.

The other two phyla of the plant kingdom, the PTERIDOPHYTA—the ferns and the SPERMAPHYTA—the seed bearing plants having cones or flowers, need not concern us here.

## BACTERIA AND FUNGI KINGDOM

These are best considered as a separate kingdom, no true position for them being found in either the plant or animal kingdoms. They are essential for the continuation of all life in maintaining the recycling of such essential materials as nitrogen and carbon. In this respect they are the most important group in a study of waste water treatment which may be regarded as a part of these natural cycles.

It is unfortunate that the popular conception of bacteria is associated with disease. Although some are responsible for certain diseases, most are beneficial in bringing about the decomposition of organic matter upon which the fertility of the soil depends. Fungi, on the other hand, popularly known by the fructifications of certain species, such as toadstools, growing in the decaying vegetation in woodlands, are more associated with the processes of decay.

*Bacteria—(Schizomycetes)* (Fission fungi)

The classification of the bacteria is based on the morphology of the cell although their biochemical activities are often used in their identification. Several classifications have been proposed, the one given in *Table* 1.2. is after one suggested by Bisset, based on morphological features (Bisset and Moore, 1952).

Certain bacteria are readily stained by the para-rosaniline dyes such as methyl-violet or gentian violet and can only be decolourized with considerable difficulty. Other species, however, do not readily take these stains and are readily decolourized. Using this distinction, a Dane by the name of Gram divided bacteria roughly into two groups:

Gram-Positive—in which the dye is retained against solvent.

Gram-Negative—in which the dye is not readily taken up and is easily lysed out by solvent.

In identification of bacteria this is a most important feature.

Other important morphological features are their size and shape; three main forms of increasing size can be recognized—coccus (spherical), bacillus (rod shaped) and spirillum (spiral) (*Fig.* 1.3). Although individual bacteria are minute (microscopic) in size, being measured in microns ($\mu = 0.001$ mm.), some form colonies of visible (macroscopic) size, e.g. the gelatinous or zöogleal colonies of *"Zöoglea ramigera"*

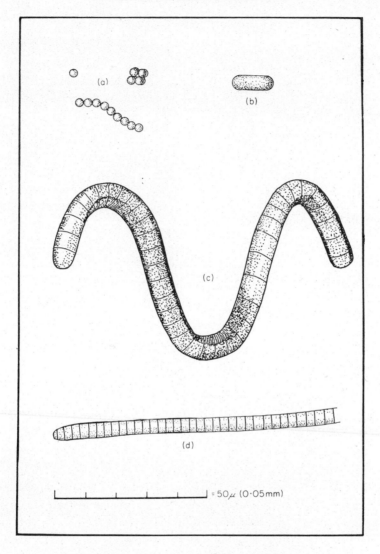

FIG. 1.3.   Forms of Bacteria.

(a)   Coccus          (c)   Spirillum
(b)   Bacillus        (d)   Filament

(*Fig.* 2.1a) and the filaments of *Sphaerotilus* (*Fig.* 2.1b) which may produce white plumose growths in flowing waters. Multiplication of bacteria is by binary fission—a simple division of one cell into two. Some are capable of producing highly resistant spores which enable them to survive adverse conditions—a further diagnostic feature.

A distinction should be made between those bacteria in the treatment plant which play an active role in the breakdown of organic matter and which are the basis of the "film" in bacteria beds and the "floc" in activated sludge and those which enter the waste water from the intestines of man and other animals. The most common of these are the *Bacterium coli* (*Bact. coli*) group (*B.* according to bacteriological terminology applying to *Bacillus*). *Bact. coli* is also known as *Escherichia coli* (*E. coli*). These are nonsporing Gram-negative rods which are normal inhabitants of the digestive tract of man and many other animals and are discharged with the faeces. Although not dangerous themselves, their presence in water does indicate faecal contamination and the possible presence of other disease producing bacteria such as *Salmonella typhi* (*Bacterium typhosa*), *Salmonella paratyphi*, the causitive organisms of typhoid fevers, other species of *Salmonella* which produce food poisoning and *Shigella*, one of the organisms responsible for dysentery. These disease producing organisms are also discharged from patients or carriers, but except at times of epidemic, are less frequent and more difficult to isolate.

*Fungi*

Like the bacteria they have simple cells devoid of chlorophyll but these are typically larger than those of bacteria and, with the exception of the yeasts, they occur in branched filaments, either septate or non-septate (*Fig.* 3.1). The filaments are known as "hyphae" and the interwoven mass of hyphae as a "mycelium", "mycology" being the study of the fungi. "Mushrooms" and "toadstools" are only the aerial fructifications formed by specialization of the mycelium of a group of fungi more advanced than those associated with treatment plants. Reproduction is typically by spores produced either sexually or asexually, the nature and arrangement of the spores and the associated elaboration of the mycelium is used as a basis for classification. Unfortunately the life cycles of some fungi are incomplete or not fully known and these are grouped together as the "fungi imperfecti"; most species of importance in treatment plants belong to this group although some belong to the Phycomycetes characterized by the non-septate hyphae.

The term "sewage fungus" which appears frequently in the literature needs some explanation. It usually refers to macroscopic growths of a collection of micro-organisms, few of which are fungi, found in organically enriched waters. These organisms include the bacteria *Sphaerotilus*, *"Zöoglea ramigera"*, *Beggiatoa* (the sulphur bacterium), and a microscopic animal (protozoan) which forms macroscopic colonies— *Carchesium*. True fungi such as *Leptomitus lacteus* and *Fusarium aqueductum* (*Fig.* 3.1.a) may be found associated with such growths but in this country are not usually the dominant organisms and are not as common as they are reported to be on the continent and in America (Butcher, 1932) (Harrison and Heukelekian, 1958). Occasionally true fungi similar to those found in bacteria beds are the dominant organisms in the sewage fungus community. Profuse growths of such fungi cover the bed of a river polluted with an industrial sewage containing metallic wastes and wastes from plastic works containing phenolic compounds and formaldehyde.

## ANIMAL KINGDOM

The animal kingdom may be divided into the animals without backbones (Invertebrates) and those with (Vertebrates). The former contains groups of animals of widely different organization which, therefore, rank as phyla, whilst the Vertebrates, although including such apparently diverse forms as fish, birds and man himself, have in fact a similar basic structural plan and are, therefore, all included in one phylum—Chordata. Although birds and sometimes rats, among the Vertebrates, frequent treatment plants, the most important animals in waste water treatment are found in the several phyla of the Invertebrates.

### Phylum Protozoa

These are microscopic animals whose body is not made up of several cells but is differentiated into different organelles which carry out the many functions of the many-celled organs of higher forms. Previously they were defined as unicellular, but are now considered non-cellular. As might be expected when we consider the three kingdoms as radiating from a common primitive form of life, some members of the lower phyla in each kingdom show marked similarities and it is, therefore, difficult to separate certain lower groups of protozoa, fungi and algae. The great diversity in the morphology, mode of locomotion and method of obtaining food, found in the protozoa, permits them to be classified into fairly well defined classes, three of which need concern us.

*Class Rhizopoda* have bodies of irregular shape which constantly changes because of the protrusion of lobe or finger-like processes known as pseudopodia. By this means they stream over the substrate and also engulf bacteria and other food material within their protoplasm. Such food matter, trapped in pockets—vacuoles—is subjected to digestive enzymes and the nutrient matter then passes into the protoplasm proper. The non-digestible portion is rejected by the protoplasm simply flowing from around it. Under adverse conditions the cell may assume a spherical shape and secrete an outer protective coat to form a cyst. In this condition it can withstand extremes of temperature and desiccation and may be dispersed aerially. *Amoeba* (*Fig.* 1.4a) is a typical example of the class. Some—Testacea—are protectively enclosed within a shell of characteristic structure, e.g. *Difflugia* (*Fig.* 1.4b) and *Arcella* (*Fig.* 2.2i).

*Class Flagellata* (Mastigophora). These have bodies of more definite shape and they move by whip-like processes known as flagella. Some, the Phytomastigina, resemble the flagellated algae in having pigments by which they are capable of photosynthesis, e.g. *Euglena* (*Fig.* 1.4c). Their abundance in organically enriched waters suggests that they are also capable of living saprophytically on dead organic matter. Other flagellates, the Zöomastigina, usually of smaller size, have no pigment and are dependent upon complex organic matter for food, e.g. *Bodo* (*Fig.* 2.2d). Although most flagellates are free-swimming, some colonial forms exist in which several individuals are attached to a common stalk, e.g. *Anthophysa* (*Fig.* 1.4d).

*Class Ciliophora*—contains species which are, on the whole, larger than those in other classes. They are characterized by the possession

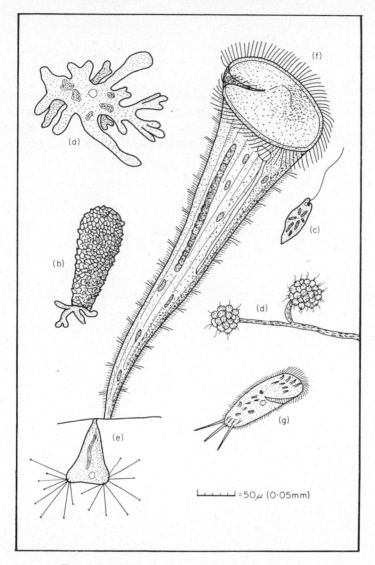

Fig. 1.4.    Some members of the phylum Protozoa.

(a)    *Amoeba*          (e)    *Acineta*
(b)    *Difflugia*       (f)    *Stentor*
(c)    *Euglena*         (g)    *Stylonychia*
(d)    *Anthophysa*

of numerous hair-like processes—cilia—which may be used in locomotion and feeding. Most species possess cilia throughout their life
and these are grouped together in the subclass Ciliata. Some, the Suctoria, although possessing cilia in the larval stages, lose them on reaching
the adult condition which is characterized by the possession of tentacles, e.g. *Acineta* (*Fig.* 1.4e).

*Sub-class Ciliata*—subdivided into orders on the distribution and
arrangement of the cilia. By rhythmic co-ordinated movements of the
cilia not only is movement effected but water currents are produced
containing bacteria and other food particles which are directed down
a groove or gullet.

*Order Holotricha*—cilia of equal size evenly distributed over the whole
of the body surface. e.g. *Paramoecium* (*Fig.* 2.2c).

*Order Heterotricha*—small cilia covering the whole of the body, but
members also possess stronger large cilia usually arranged in spiral
bands around the body, e.g. *Stentor*, (*Fig.* 1.4f).

*Order Hypotricha*—flattened organism, with a ventral gullet. The
cilia are mostly confined to the ventral surface and are highly specialized as thick cirri which do not move rhythmically but act as stilt-like
legs by which they creep over the substrate. The number and arrangement of these cirri are important features in specific identification, e.g.
*Stylonychia* (*Fig.* 1.4g).

*Order Peritricha* have the cilia restricted to a peristomal spiral. The
individuals are bell-shaped and sessile, being attached by a stalk which
is usually contractile e.g. *Vorticella* (*Fig.* 2.2a & b). Many form colonies, the individuals being borne at the end of the multi-branched
stalks, e.g. *Carchesium*.

In contrast with the non-cellular structure of the protozoa, the other
animals have bodies composed of many cells which are differently
modified for various functions; all such animals are referred to as
"Metazoa".

*Phylum Platyhelminthes* (Flatworms)

These are small flat unsegmented worms of simple structure having only one opening into the food canal which is usually much branched. This well defined group of worms is divided into three classes, one of which (Turbellaria) have members which are free living and are to be found in fresh-water streams e.g. *Planaria* spp. *Polycelis* spp. (*Fig.* 1.5a) and *Dendrocoelum lacteum* (*Fig.* 1.5b). The other two classes are parasitic and show varying degrees of modification to this mode of life, the Trematoda (flukes) being less modified than the Cestoda (tapeworms). The latter are elongate ribbon-like worms parasitic in

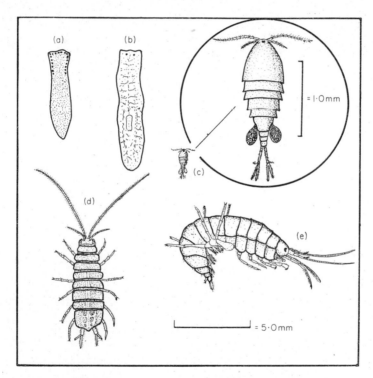

FIG. 1.5.   Some Invertebrate animals of the phyla.

Platyhelminthes                     Anthropoda
   (a) *Polycelis nigra*            (c) *Cyclops*
   (b) *Dendrocoelum lacteum*        (d) *Asellus aquaticus*
                                     (e) *Gammarus pulex*

the gut of vertebrates, including man. They appear segmented but a study of their structure and development shows that they consist of a small head or scolex which is provided with suckers and hooks whereby the parasite is firmly attached to the gut wall of the host. Behind the head, segments known as proglottides are proliferated; as these pass backwards they enlarge and when mature, each is seen to contain a full set of sex organs. Thus each proglottis is comparable with one

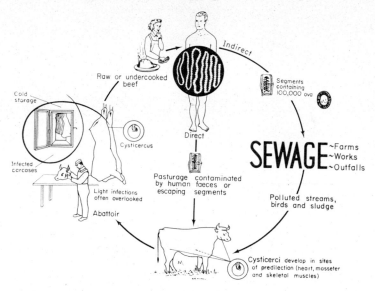

FIG. 1.6. "The life-cycle of the beef tapeworm, *Taenia saginata*" (From Silverman, P.H. (1955). The survival of the egg of the 'Beef Tapeworm'. *Taenia saginata*. The Biology of Sewers and Sewage Treatment, *Advanc. Sci.*, London, **12**. 109—reproduced by kind permission of author and editor).

flat worm, the whole tapeworm being considered as a chain of individuals of varying degrees of maturity. The beef tapeworm *Taenia saginata*—a parasite of man—may reach a length of twenty feet!

Apart from structural modifications for the parasitic mode of life, parasites, to ensure the reinfection of a suitable host, produce large numbers of eggs and may have complicated life histories. The tapeworm *T. saginata* may be taken as an example (*Fig.* 1.6). After fertilization, the eggs develop into an embryo having six hooks known as a hexacanth, whilst still within the proglottis. The ripe proglottides containing thousands of these embryos, each still enclosed in the egg membranes, are discharged from the human host after becoming detached from the end of the tapeworm. No further development takes place until they are eaten by a suitable secondary host—cattle in this

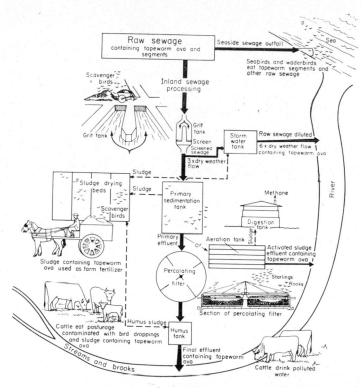

FIG. 1.7. "Possible methods by which tape-worm eggs may be disseminated in sewage treatment." (From Silverman, P.H., (1955). The survival of the egg of the 'Beef Tapeworm' *Taenia saginata*. The Biology of Sewers and Sewage Treatment. *Advanc. Sci.*, London, **12**, 110—reproduced by kind permission of author and editor).

case. Within the gut of cattle, the egg membranes disintegrate under the successive action of gastric and intestinal juices to liberate the embryos, which then make their way via the blood stream to the muscles where each develops into a cysticercus or bladder worm. Further development only takes place if the infected meat is eaten raw or insufficiently cooked to kill the cysticerci; in this event, the bladder is digested and the scolex, previously developed as an invagination of the bladder, becomes attached to the intestine wall and commences to proliferate proglottides, thus completing the cycle.

It has been shown that viable tapeworm eggs are capable of passing through most treatment processes even including sand filters and micro-strainers. Silverman and Griffiths (1955) have produced evidence to suggest that the increase in bovine cysticercosis caused by the bladder worm stage of *T. saginata* in cattle, since the Second World War, may be due to overloaded treatment plants. The mild nature of the infections suggest a wide dissemination of eggs such as would be possible in a sewage effluent. Only a few infected people in a drainage area are needed to supply eggs sufficient to infect a large number of cattle. The possible methods of contamination are illustrated in *Fig*. 1.7.

### Phylum Nematoda—(Roundworms)

These are unsegmented worms having spindle or thread-like bodies pointed at both ends. The phylum includes parasitic and free-living forms. The parasitic forms have received much attention including the eelworms, parasitic on crops, and the larger ones parasitic in man. They are capable of prolific egg production; these pass out with the faeces of the host and their possible dissemination in sewage effluents and sludge must be considered. The free-living forms inhabiting soils and fresh water have attracted less attention, although their importance in maintaining soil fertility has been demonstrated by Overgaard (1949) and their presence in fresh water and waste water treatment plants is probably equally significant. The free living forms are usually small, the average size being 1 mm (*Fig*. 2.1e). Their movements are characteristic; unlike the true worms which move by alternate stretching and contraction, they progress in S shaped curves of the body, which remains of constant diameter. Although readily recognized as a group, the different species are not readily distinguished.

### Phylum Rotifera (Wheel animalcules)

These are minute unsegmented animals characterized by the presence of a ciliated structure anteriorly—the corona—which is used in feeding and locomotion. In many, this takes the form of two flat discs (*Fig*.

2.1f). Most species live in fresh water and are able to withstand being dried up by forming cysts in which form they are probably dispersed by the wind. Besides normal sexual reproduction, the eggs are capable of developing without being fertilized, a phenomenon known as parthenogenesis. In some, parthenogenetic and sexual reproduction alternate and coincide with the seasons; fertilized eggs which develop thick shells are produced in the autumn and these remain dormant throughout the winter and develop the following spring. In one family, which includes the common genus *Rotifer*, no males have ever been found, and in others they are minute and degenerate.

*Phylum Annelida (True worms)*

Soft bodied worms showing segmentation externally as a series of rings, the body wall being covered by a thin cuticle which is not hardened as in insects. The two classes occurring in fresh waters are readily distinguished—the Oligochaetae which are characterized by the presence of bristles (chaetae) on most segments and include the common earthworm and related species, and the Hirudinea (Leeches) which have no chaetae but possess two suckers, one anterior and a more obvious one posterior. They are also more flattened than the worms. Most are ectoparasites sucking the blood of other animals but some eat small aquatic animals.

*Class Oligochaeta*—is divided into eight families mainly on the basis of the number and shape of the chaetae which are arranged in four bundles—two on the dorsal (upper) surface and two ventrally (lower). Four of these families contain members which may occur in waste water treatment plants. The Lumbricidae are readily recognized by their larger size and their similarity to the common earthworm which is a terrestrial member of this family. The common brandling *Eisenia foetida* and *Lumbricus rubellus* are present in many bacteria beds treating domestic sewage. Members of the other families are much thinner. The Tubificidae construct tubes from mud from which their posterior portions protrude and wave around; many possess red blood which can be seen through the body wall. They are usually more than 3 cm long and may be as long as 20 cm. They usually have more than two bristles per bundle, the ventral ones being curved and having cleft tips. The

3

Enchytraeidae (pot worms) are smaller (less than 3·5 cm) and are creamy white in colour. As with the Tubificidae there are usually more than two bristles per bundle but these are simple pointed. In this order *Lumbricillus (Pachydrilus) lineatus (Fig.* 3.2d) is a very common member of the bacteria bed fauna. In another family, the Aelosomatidae, the organisms are only a few mm long and are characterized by highly coloured bodies contained in their integument and the presence of numerous long hair-like bristles. Young worms are budded off posteriorly and a chain of individuals may sometimes be found. A species of *Aelosoma* having pink bodies in the integument, may be so abundant in activated sludge that they impart a pink colouration to the surface of the settled sludge. Under adverse conditions they are able to form resistant cysts and thus are able to withstand periods of desiccation.

*Phylum Arthropoda*

Members of this successful phylum are characterized by having a segmented body possessing a hard protective outer cuticle, each segment typically having a pair of jointed appendages. These appendages are differently modified in the different groups to perform such functions as locomotion, respiration, food capture and mastication and sensory perception. Because of the hard external skeleton, growth occurs by a series of moults, or ecdyses, by which the outer skin is shed and the new cuticle, formed beneath, only hardening after the creature has expanded. The discarded casts are quite thin since much of the material in the cuticle is re-absorbed for use in the new cuticle. As a group they are the most successful invertebrates and are probably man's most serious competitors on earth. Of the six classes into which the phylum is divided, representatives from four may be found in waste treatment plants, of the other two, one forms an interesting evolutionary link with the Annelida and the other (Trilobita) contains only fossils. Although the species found in treatment plants are confined to a small number of the many orders in the Arthropoda, a fairly full classification is given, as they are of importance in stream ecology, a matter which should also concern the waste water engineer.

*Class Crustacea*—these are nearly all aquatic organisms and are best known as marine forms such as crabs, lobsters and shrimps. The few species associated with treatment plants, however, belong to the more primitive orders and are also much smaller, *Cyclops* (*Fig.* 1.5c) being less than 2 mm long, another, *Asellus aquaticus* (water hog louse) (*Fig.* 1.5d) is about 2 cm long.

*Class Insecta*—consists of arthropods in which the body of the adult is divided into three sections—head, thorax and abdomen. Typically, there are two pairs of wings arising from the thorax and three pairs of walking legs also attached to the thorax. The class is divided into two sub-classes—one small group of primitive wingless insects—the Apterygota, which includes the silverfish and springtails (*Fig.* 3.2f) and a much larger group—the Pterygota—which possess wings or have lost them secondarily in evolution. The Apterygota have a simple life cycle, the eggs hatching into forms resembling the adults, but in the Pterygota the life cycle is more complicated. In the most complicated type, the egg hatches into a larva, the maggot of a fly, or caterpillar of a butterfly. This stage is the active feeding and growing stage of the insect. After a specific number of moults the insect enters what appears to be a resting stage—the pupa or chrysalis, which differs considerably in form from the larva. Within the protective thickened cuticle, however, a reorganization is taking place, for after a period the adult insect—the imago—emerges from the pupal case. These remarkable changes in appearance of the insect at the different stages are known as metamorphoses (*Fig.* 3.2). These orders of insects having this complete life cycle—eggs, larva, pupa, imago—are grouped together in the Endopterygota—wings developing internally. Other orders of the Pterygota, however, have a shortened cycle—the pupal stage being absent and the larval stage showing some resemblance to the adult and known as nymphs; these are grouped together in the Exopterygota—wings developing externally. The order Diptera (the true flies) have only one pair of wings, the second pair having been modified as club shaped structures—the halteres—used as balancing organs. They have a full life cycle and the larvae never possess true jointed legs on the thorax although they may have thick fleshy false legs—prolegs—on thorax or abdomen. (*Fig.* 3.2).

*Class Arachnida*—(scorpions, spiders and mites)—these are readily distinguished from the insects in having four pairs of walking legs

3*

and they are not divided into head, thorax and abdomen. In the spiders the body is divided into two by a narrow waist; the mites have rounded bodies with no division (*Fig.* 3.2e).

Sometimes linked with the Arachnida—although of doubtful affinity, are the "bear animalcules"—the Tardigrada, which are sometimes found in the film from bacteria beds. They are microscopic in size and have unsegmented bodies carrying four pairs of unjointed stumpy legs.

*Phylum Mollusca* (the snails, slugs, limpets and mussels)

This Phylum consists of soft-bodied animals showing no sign of segmentation in the adult. The body is usually protected with a shell into which the whole animal can withdraw. Two classes are represented in fresh water; the Gastropoda, including the snails and limpets, have a shell in one piece, and the Lamellibranchiata including mussels and cockles, in which the shell is bi-valved.

## PHYSIOLOGY

Although it is desirable to be able to identify and classify an organism, it is the functioning and activity of the organism that is of importance in determining its role in waste water treatment. By what means does it obtain its life energy and what are the end products of its activity? Physiology is the branch of biology which includes this aspect of the subject. The biochemical processes involved in the functioning and activity of organisms are known collectively as METABOLISM. Those involved in the breakdown of complex matter to simpler products are known as KATABOLISM and the reverse process of synthesis of complex matter from simpler substances as ANABOLISM. Chemical reactions involved in metabolism proceed at much greater rates than could be expected for the reactions involved and the necessary limitations on extreme temperature and pressure, imposed by the living cells. Such reaction rates are made possible by the presence of numerous catalysts, i.e. substances which affect the *rate* of a chemical reaction but which themselves remain unchanged at the end of the reaction. Such organic catalysts which are proteinaceous compounds produced by the living cell are known as ENZYMES. As catalysts they only affect the rate at which the reaction proceeds and do not influence the course or the equilibrium of the reaction. The importance of enzymes in cell metabolism and, therefore, in waste water treatment in which the waste is used as a metabolite, warrants some consideration being given to their properties and factors influencing their activity.

*Specificity*—Enzymes are remarkably specific in their activities, a given enzyme being capable of catalysing one, or at most few, reactions. Thus numerous enzymes are required to catalyse the wide range of metabolic processes occurring within the cell.

*Temperature*—The effect of temperature on enzymatic activity is the resultant of two opposing factors. Like most chemical reactions the reaction velocity increases with rise in temperature but the higher the temperature the less stable the enzymes become. Thus, above a certain temperature, called the optimum temperature, the thermal inactivation of the enzymes, due probably to the thermal denaturing of the proteins, more than offsets the resultant increase in the reaction velocity and results in a rapid decrease in enzymatic activity. The effect of thermal inactivation is also a function of time and, as pointed out by Baldwin (1959), in determining the optimum temperature, the time factor must be taken into account. In tests of short duration during which the enzymes do not need to be long-lived, much higher "optimum" temperatures may be recorded than in tests of longer duration in which the effects of enzyme inactivation become evident. The latter tests are, of course, more applicable in waste water treatment where sustained microbial activity is required.

*pH*—A given enzyme is only active over a fairly narrow range of pH within which activity increases to a maximum at a definite pH— the optimum—and then declines again. Changes in enzyme activity around the optimum are probably due to the resultant changes in the ionic state of the enzyme and these changes are usually reversible. The marked reductions in activity towards the limits of the pH range, however, are the result of the de-activation of the enzymes due to the irreversible denaturing of the proteins. Unlike the effects of temperature, the stability of the enzyme is usually greatest about the optimum pH. Each enzyme thus has its characteristic optimum pH, although this may vary somewhat with the nature of the substrate due to the indirect effect of pH on the degree of dissociation of the compound concerned.

*Protein precipitants*—Enzymes are active in the colloidal state and substances which bring about their precipitation by forming insoluble salts with them, inhibit their activity. Thus substances such as the heavy metals and alkaloid reagents, which form insoluble salts with proteins, are powerful inhibitors of enzyme activity. Other forces which bring about protein denaturation such as violent mechanical agitation or ultra-violet radiation, also cause the inactivation of enzymes.

*Concentration*—Although enzymes are effective at very low concentrations, their concentration in relation to the concentration of substrate may be a limiting factor affecting the rate of a reaction. To understand this effect it is necessary to appreciate the mechanism by which enzymes are considered to act. It is now thought that the enzyme (E) and the substrate (S) react together to form an unstable complex (ES). In this form the substrate molecule is considered to be more reactive and is said to have been "activated" by the enzyme. The substrate-enzyme complex is then broken down producing the end products (P and Q), the enzyme (E) again being liberated (Baldwin, 1959).

$$E + S \rightleftharpoons ES \rightarrow E + P + Q$$

The rate of the reaction is dependent upon the molecular concentration of the unstable complex $(ES)$ which is in turn dependent upon both the concentration of the substrate $(S)$ and that of the enzyme $(E)$. With low concentrations of substrate, as in most waste waters, increase in the concentration of the substrate results in an increase in reaction velocity until a value is reached, the saturation point of the enzyme when enzyme concentration becomes limiting.

*Activators and Co-enzymes*—Many enzymes are incapable of catalytic activity unless certain other substances are present. Baldwin (1959) distinguishes between two groups of such accessory substances. Those needed to enable the enzyme to activate the substrate and which are, therefore, an essential part of the activating system, are known as ACTIVATORS. Metallic ions such as Mn, Mo, Zn and Co required as "trace" elements by most organisms are thought to act as such activators in enzyme systems. Even though the substrate may be successfully activated, the subsequent reaction may not proceed unless other accessory substances are present. This second group of accessory substances, which take part in the subsequent reaction, are known as CO-ENZYMES. These are nonproteinaceous, thermostable substances, examples of which will be met with in the subsequent outline of respiratory processes.

*Classification*—Although enzymes are produced inside the cell, some are secreted by the cell to act on an external substrate. These are known as extra-cellular enzymes in contrast to those which catalyse reactions within the cell—the intracellular enzymes. They are also classified on the type of reaction they catalyse. Hydrolases, for example, are enzymes concerned with the hydrolysis of organic matter, an important process in digestion, whereby food is rendered available as a respiratory substrate for the cell. Most extracellular enzymes fall into this group. Another important group are the dehydrogenases which catalyse the dehydrogenation of organic substrates in the process of respiration.

*Respiration*

Basically, the energy needed for life processes is obtained by the oxidation of an oxidizable substance (the combustion of a fuel) by the process of respiration. The oxidation of one substance necessarily results in the reduction of another and a biological oxidation-reduction reaction may be regarded as the transfer of hydrogen atoms (or of electrons) from the substance oxidized (the H-donor) to the one reduced (the H-acceptor).

$$AH_2 \quad + \quad B \quad \rightarrow \quad A \quad + \quad BH_2$$
(H-Donor)  (H-acceptor)

The initial dehydrogenation is catalysed by enzymes of the dehydrogenase group and the transference of the hydrogen takes place via one or more intermediate carriers—co-enzymes—which form what is termed a respiratory pathway. One possible respiratory pathway, involving several such co-enzymes, is shown in *Fig*. 1.8. The initial hydrogen acceptor in the katabolic oxidation of the organic matter ($AH_2$) is diphospho-pyridine-nucleotide (DPN), sometimes known as co-enzyme I. From this the H is transferred to a second co-enzyme, flavin-adenine-dinucleotide (FAD). The final steps in the path involve what

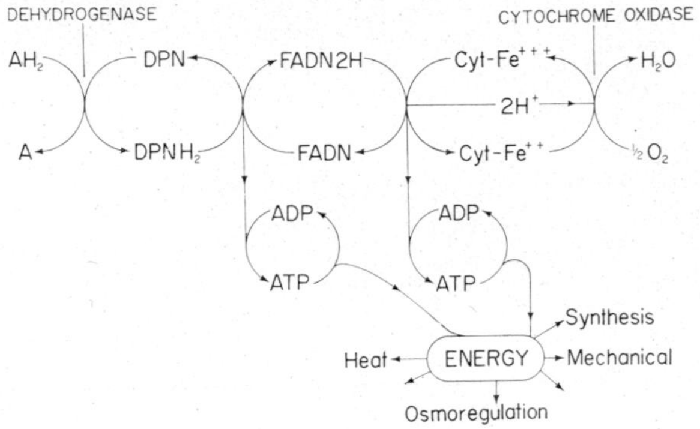

Fig. 1.8. A respiratory pathway involving several coenzymes involved in the dehydrogenation of an organic substrate $AH_2$ and the transference of the energy produced to the energy consuming activities of the cell.

is known as the cytochrome system. Cytochrome is an iron-containing enzyme and it is thought that the oxidation/reduction reaction concerned involves the transfer of one electron and the change from the ferric state ($Fe^{+++}$) to the ferrous state ($Fe^{++}$).

$$Cytochrome—Fe^{+++} + e \rightarrow Cytochrome—Fe^{++}$$

When the cytochrome accepts one electron a hydrogen ion ($H^+$) is released

$$Cytochrome—Fe^{+++} + H \rightarrow Cytochrome—Fe^{++} + H^+$$

The reduced cytochrome is finally oxidized by atmospheric oxygen by losing an electron, the released hydrogen ion ($H^+$) being removed in the process.

Along such pathways the energy yielded by the oxidation of the substrate is released at different stages as the hydrogen is "stepped down". This released energy is not, however, directly available for the organism's activities but has to be trapped and stored as chemical energy for subsequent use. This is achieved by a substance which participates in both the exothermic (energy producing) reactions of respiration and the endothermic (energy consuming) reactions involved in the many activities of the organism, thus coupling them together. The release of energy along the respiratory pathway is associated with the production of compounds having high-energy-phosphate bonds which convert the low-energy co-enzyme, adenosine-diphosphate (ADP), to the high-energy co-enzyme, adenosine-triphosphate (ATP) thus storing the energy, the process being known as oxidative phosphorylation. The ATP then participates in the endothermic reactions of the cells associated with the several activities of the organism, releasing the stored energy in being broken down into ADP and the inorganic phosphate again (*Fig.* 1.8).

In aerobic organisms—ones living in the presence of atmospheric oxygen—oxygen acts as the ultimate hydrogen acceptor.

$$AH_2 + \tfrac{1}{2}O_2 \rightarrow A + H_2O$$

$$\text{e.g.} \quad C_6H_{12}O_6 + 6O_2 \rightarrow 6CO_2 + 6H_2O$$
$$\text{(glucose) (oxygen) (carbon} \quad \text{(water)}$$
$$\text{dioxide)}$$

In anaerobic organisms—those able to live in the absence of atmospheric oxygen—the ultimate hydrogen acceptor is either an organic byproduct of the breakdown process which is thereby reduced:

$$AH_2B \rightarrow A + BH_2$$

$$\text{e.g.} \quad C_6H_{12}O_6 \rightarrow 2CO_2 + 2CH_3CH_2OH$$
$$\text{(glucose)} \quad \text{(carbon} \quad \text{(ethyl alcohol)}$$
$$\text{dioxide)}$$

or a reducible substance in the substrate such as nitrate, bringing about de-nitrification:

$$4AH_2 + HNO_3 \rightarrow 4A + NH_3 + 3H_2O$$

Thus aerobic and anaerobic respiration differ essentially only in the nature of the ultimate hydrogen acceptor, although the anaerobic process does not bring about complete oxidation of the organic matter, and liberates less energy. The respiratory enzymes which bring about these different reactions are sensitive to many poisons such as cyanide, carbon monoxide and hydrogen sulphide and such substances act as respiratory poisons by inactivating a link in the chain of respiratory enzymes.

Apart from providing the fuel for respiration, an organism requires basic materials for the synthesis of new protoplasm, both to replace worn out protoplasm and to produce additional protoplasm in growth. The energy needed for this synthesis is usually provided by respiration through the ADP-ATP system. The synthesis of protoplasm is reversible in as much as in the absence of external food, the cell utilizes the protoplasm as respiratory substrate to provide the energy necessary to maintain life. This form of respiration, where the cell's protoplasm is used as a respiratory substrate, is known as ENDOGENOUS RESPIRATION. There is some doubt as to whether this endogenous respiration goes on in the presence of external food, when the resultant reduction in protoplasm would be masked by the much greater synthesis of protoplasm by the energy released from the respiration of external food, or whether protoplasm is only used under starvation conditions. The wide use of the term "endogenous" in connection with microbial cultures will be discussed later.

It is essential to realize that energy production by respiration is a function of each individual living cell of the organism. Different bodies within the cell have been associated with different metabolic activities. There is evidence, for example, that certain cellular bodies, known as mitochondria, are the principal site of oxidative phosphorylation. The necessary reactants, the substrate and oxygen, must therefore first enter the cell. The method by which this is achieved and the nature and source of the primary energy producing compounds can be used to divide organisms into different nutritional groups. This grouping, as we shall see, is more important in determining interrelationships between populations than is the systematic classification. All organisms may be divided into two groups on the basis of their basic food requirements. AUTOTROPHIC forms do not use organic compounds as primary sources of energy; they are able to synthesize organic compounds from carbon dioxide using either light energy (PHOTOSYNTHESIS) or energy from inorganic chemical reactions (CHEMOSYNTHESIS). HETEROTROPHIC organisms are incapable of such synthesis and require organic compounds as their primary source of energy, and are, therefore, dependent upon autotrophic organisms either directly or indirectly for such food (Lees, 1955).

The most important autotrophic organisms are plants which, using their pigments, are able to store light energy from the sun as chemical energy in organic compounds. The process, in which carbon dioxide is the sole source of carbon, and oxygen is produced as a by-product, is known as PHOTOSYNTHESIS.

$$\text{Light energy}$$
$$6CO_2 + 6H_2O \quad \rightarrow \quad C_6H_{12}O_6 + 6O_2$$
(Carbon
dioxide) (water) (glucose) (oxygen)

Besides plants, some pigment–bearing bacteria—the photosynthetic bacteria—are also able to utilize light energy for synthesis but instead of oxygen being produced an inorganic oxidation takes place.

$$\text{Light energy}$$
e.g. $3H_2S + 6H_2O + 6CO_2 \quad \rightarrow \quad C_6H_{12}O_6 + 3H_2SO_4$
(Hydrogen (Sulphuric
sulphide) acid)

Other autotrophic bacteria utilize the energy of inorganic chemical reactions, the process being known as CHEMOSYNTHESIS.

e.g. *Nitrosomonas* $NH_3 + 1\frac{1}{2}O_2 \rightarrow HNO_2 + H_2O + $ ENERGY.
ammonia nitrous acid

*Nitrobacter* $NO_2 + \frac{1}{2}O_2 \rightarrow NO_3 + $ ENERGY.
nitrite nitrate

*Beggiatoa.* $H_2S + \frac{1}{2}O_2 \quad \rightarrow \quad S + H_2O + $ ENERGY
sulphur

In the case of *Beggiatoa*, the sulphur is deposited as granules within the cells and when sulphide is no longer available it is then oxidized to sulphate liberating more energy:

$$S + 1\frac{1}{2}O_2 + H_2O \quad \rightarrow \quad H_2SO_4 + \text{ENERGY}$$

Autotrophic organisms take in their inorganic nutrients in solution. In the higher plants the $CO_2$ from the atmosphere enters the leaves through openings (stomata) and then passes into the cells in solution. The other basic nutrients such as mineral salts, including nitrogen as nitrate, are absorbed by the root system and pass to the individual cells by means of a vascular system. In the lower plants such as the algae, and in the autotrophic bacteria where the individual cells are bathed in a solution of nutrients, these enter the cells directly in solution.

In heterotrophic forms the nature of the organic food and the method by which it enters the cells differ considerably. In the metazoa, particulate and soluble food material is taken into an alimentary (food) canal in which the utilizable organic matter is rendered soluble by extra-cellular enzymes before being absorbed by the cells of the gut wall and then transported via the blood system to other cells of the animal. The material remaining unabsorbed by the digestive processes is passed out of the animal as faeces. Some protozoa use a similar method; *Paramoecium* ingests particulate food (bacteria), contained in a drop of water, through a gullet into the protoplasm where it can be seen as a vacuole into which digestive enzymes are secreted and the utilizable food is absorbed into the protoplasm, the unabsorbed material being ejected from the organism.

The heterotrophic bacteria and fungi take in their organic food in solution. In the case of colloidal and particulate matter suspended in water, as in some waste waters, this is first *ad*sorbed on to the outer surface of the bacterial or fungal cell. Enzymes are then secreted through the cell wall which render the utilizable organic matter capable of being absorbed into the cell. The structure of the cell membranes of micro-organisms thus play an important role in the initial *ad*sorption and the subsequent selective *ab*sorption of the substrate. *Figure* 1.9 is a diagrammatic representation of the enveloping membranes of a typical bacterial cell.

Structurally the main pellicle enclosing the cytoplasm, nuclear material and other cytoplasmic contents, is the cell wall. This is predominantly polysaccharide of low chemical reactivity and determines the shape of the cell. Often, to the outside of the cell wall is a slime layer of varying thickness forming a capsule. Functionally, however, in controlling the interchange of materials between the cell and the outside, another membrane is involved. This lies within the cell wall and surrounds the cytoplasm and is known as the cytoplasmic membrane. It is a thin, although tough membrane, predominantly lipo-protein, and unlike the permeable cell wall and capsule, it is semi-permeable, selectively absorbing certain molecules.

More important ecologically than the method of food intake is the nature of the food. It is necessary to distinguish between those heterotrophic forms which obtain their organic matter by preying on other living organisms either plant or animal, thereby affecting the population of the latter, and those which obtain their organic matter in the

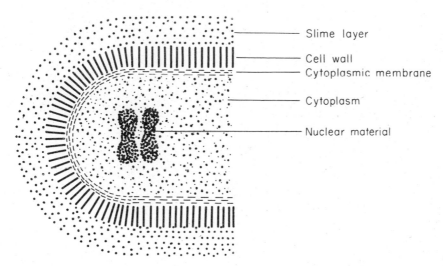

Slime layer
Cell wall
Cytoplasmic membrane
Cytoplasm
Nuclear material

FIG. 1.9.   The enveloping membranes of a typical bacterial cell.

form of dead or decaying matter. In the present work the former group —mostly animals—which utilize living matter, will be termed *holozoic*, and the latter, those utilizing dead and decaying matter will be termed *saprobic*. Saprobic forms may be further divided into those, mostly animals, which ingest particulate decaying matter—(*saprozoic*), and those which, like bacteria and fungi, absorb the organic matter in soluble form—(*saprophytic*). The reader is warned that these terms have been used rather loosely in the literature; holozoic for example is often used synonymously with heterotrophic, the term holophytic being the corresponding synonym for autotrophic. Saprozoic and saprophytic are also used synonymously. For our purpose, however, rather than introduce new nutritional terminology into a field already thick with it, we shall use the existing terms in the limited sense defined above.

The oxygen needed in respiration must also enter the cell. In the case of aquatic micro-organisms it enters in solution from the surrounding water in which it is dissolved. In the metazoa the oxygen must be transported to the individual cells from the exterior. In some, the oxygen is taken in through all of the moist body surface, e.g. worms, in others, special areas of the surface are modified for gaseous exchange such as gills and lungs. From these respiratory surfaces the oxygen is transported in the blood system—usually chemically combined with a respiratory pigment such as haemoglobin—to the tissues, where the oxygen is given up to the respiring cells via the fluids in which they are bathed. Insects, most of which are aerial or terrestrial and need to conserve the water within their bodies, would be at a disadvantage if they had moist areas exposed for respiratory exchange. They have in fact evolved an interconnecting system of tubes—trachea—through which the gaseous oxygen penetrates the tissues of the body. The trachea open to the outside through spiracles, the frequency of the opening and closing of which controls the loss of water. Some aquatic metazoa also obtain oxygen from that dissolved in the water in which they live, a few are dependent on atmospheric oxygen and need to live associated with the surface of the water (mosquito larvae and pupae) or visit it from time to time (diving beetles). In plants, the oxygen produced by photosynthesis may supply their respiratory needs and often a surplus of oxygen is given off. In darkness, however, plants need to utilize oxygen from without and in an aquatic environment this may result in diurnal fluctuations in the amount of dissolved oxygen.

*Excretion*

In respiration, as in all forms of combustion, waste products are produced and these have to be removed from the sphere of activity in the cell where their accumulation would prove harmful. The mechanism of removal of these waste products, known as excretion, differs widely. The two chief excretory products are those resulting from the oxidation of carbohydrates (carbon dioxide, water) and those from proteins (ammonia, uric acid, urea). In plant and animals the $CO_2$ passes out via the reverse path to that by which the oxygen is taken in. In plants this path is also taken by the water. Animals, however, are characterized by also producing nitrogenous waste materials. These are usually excreted in solution, together with water and salts, through special excretory organs corresponding to the kidneys of vertebrates. The waste products in the metazoa are transported from the cells to these organs of excretion via the blood system. In insects, because of their need to conserve water, although the nitrogenous waste is secreted into the excretory tubule as a soluble urate, this is converted into crystals of uric acid which is relatively insoluble, before passing into the hind gut to be discharged as a solid with the faeces; the water and inorganic base (potassium and sodium bicarbonate) remain within the insect.

Apart from excretory functions, these organs are also responsible for the maintenance of the salinity concentration of the body fluids necessary for the proper functioning of the cells. When solutions of different concentrations are separated by a semi-permeable membrane, i.e. one which is more permeable to water than to the solute, water will pass from the stronger solution to the weaker by a process known as osmosis; the stronger solution is said to have a higher osmotic pressure. Cell membranes act as semi-permeable membranes and if the cell content has a higher osmotic pressure than the outside medium, water will tend to pass into the cell. If, on the other hand, the external medium has a higher osmotic pressure, water will be extracted from the cell. Within plant cells having rigid cellulose walls, a turgor pressure is developed which limits the entry of water. When such cells are placed in stronger solutions water passes out of the cell and the cytoplasm within the cytoplasmic membrane contracts away from the cell wall—a phenomenon known as plasmolysis: when replaced in a weaker solution of lower osmotic pressure than the cell contents, water is again taken in and the cytoplasm swells to fill the cell which again becomes turgid. Bacteria are reported to act in a similar way (Bisset, 1950) and are, therefore, able to withstand fairly wide changes in the osmotic pressure of their environment. The animal cell, however, having no such rigid wall, would burst if the internal osmotic pressure was much greater than that of the external medium, were it not for the presence of a mechanism to remove the excess water from the cell. Lower forms of marine invertebrate animals have internal body fluids which are of similar concentration to the sea water and are able to adjust it to the small changes in salinity of the sea. No osmo-regulatory mechanism is, therefore, needed and the organisms are said to be "stenohaline", their body fluids being in osmotic equilibrium with the surrounding medium. In fresh water animals the osmotic pressure of the body fluids is higher than that of the medium and thus they tend to absorb water from their surroundings. In such animals a method of osmo-regulation is necessary to excrete the excess water, this process usually being performed by the excretory organ. In protozoa for example the contractile vacuoles are probably more important as osmotic regulators than in nitrogenous excretion; they are usually only found in fresh water species. Fresh water animals are therefore osmotically independent of their surrounding medium, but to be so, they have to expend energy in the process of osmo-regulation.

## ECOLOGY

Although physiology gives us an understanding of the functional processes of organisms and the way in which organic wastes may be broken down, in treatment plants, organisms do not exist in the waste as pure cultures but as communities of varying degrees of complexity. Thus a knowledge is needed not only of the requirements of the individual organisms but of the inter-relationships between populations and factors controlling the growth and activity of populations. Ecology is that branch of biological study which deals with these different aspects.

Historically, ecology was at first solely concerned with the collecting and recording of organisms and sometimes the linking of these with the observed environmental factors. It could then have been defined as "scientific natural history". Plant ecology and animal ecology have developed as separate subjects in this country. Although we shall need to concern ourselves with communities containing animals and plants (including bacteria and fungi), it is certain principles evolved from studies in animal ecology, that are more important for our immediate purpose. The publication of Elton's *Animal Ecology* in 1927 focused attention on the community rather than the individual as a unit for study. Since then it has been put on a quantitative basis and has led to the present day "population dynamics". A further development has been the study of the transference of materials and energy between populations—called "functional synecology" or "productivity ecology" (Macfadyen, 1957).

The environmental factors affecting an organism and limiting its distribution, and in some cases its population, may be considered under three ill-defined headings; (I) Physical, (II) Chemical and (III) Biotic. The physical factors include the physical nature of the habitat, aquatic, terrestrial or subaerial, etc., and such climatic factors as temperature, light and humidity. The movement of the medium, such as wind speeds and the velocity of water currents are also important physical factors in the environment of some species. Chemical factors would appear to be more important in the aquatic and subterrestrial habitats where such factors as pH, calcium and oxygen content, salinity and the presence of toxic substances may all affect different species differentially. Biotic factors are those involving the inter-relationship with other organisms. These include the predator-prey relationship, both between animal and plant and between animal and animal. In such relationships, the population of the prey may be affected by the activity of the predator, and conversely, the abundance of the prey may determine the population of the predator species it can support. Competition for a limited common food supply, either between individuals of the same species (intraspecific competition), or between different species (interspecific competition), is another important biotic factor. In dense communities similar competition may exist for oxygen and for actual living space. The availability of food other than prey may also be considered a biotic factor. Non-living organic matter is thus a biotic factor in the environment of saprobic organisms although it also contributes to the chemical environment.

In addition to creating biotic pressures, the activity of a population may affect the chemical and physical environment; indeed waste water treatment may be regarded as resulting from the activity of organisms on one component of their environment—the waste being treated. The resultant change in the environment may be unfavourable to the population bringing it about and more favourable to another species, which thereby replaces it. The repetition of this process causes a succession of dominant species, a phenomenon known as an "ecological succession". Evidence of such a succession can be readily witnessed by allowing sewage to stand in an open beaker in a window. Successions may occur in relation to time or distance. As sewage is purified in percolat-

4

ing downward through a bacteria bed different species become dominant. A similar succession of dominant species occurs along the length of an organically polluted stream as self-purification proceeds. Ecological successions may also result from environmental changes brought about by causes other than biotic ones. The gradual erosion or silting of a stretch of stream bed, for example, will result in a succession of dominant species.

The earlier type of ecology—autecology—involving the correlation of the distribution of one species with environmental factors and the associated experimental work, has enabled certain physical and chemical tolerance limits within which the species exists to be determined. In some cases the optimum of such conditions, the preferendum, has also been determined. The laboratory aspect of this work is, however, of limited practical value. In its natural habitat the organism is subjected simultaneously to several factors, the joint effect of which is not necessarily additive because of the interaction of the factors involved. Consider, for example, the interaction of two toxic substances associated with sewage effluents, ammonia and carbon dioxide. The toxicity of ammonia is greater when it is present in the un-ionized form ($NH_3$) than when as the ion $NH_4^+$. The degree of dissociation is greater at lower pH values and thus the presence of carbon dioxide which reduces the pH reduces the toxicity of ammonia.

It is now recognized that an ecological niche cannot be defined simply by the combination of a few physical and chemical factors. A fresh-water biologist with all his knowledge of the physico-chemical requirements of a species of fish is less likely to locate them in a given stream than is an experienced fisherman with his intuitive knowledge of their haunts and habits. In waste water treatment, laboratory tests have been of use in determining the wider limits of the conditions under which certain organisms might be expected to thrive. The optimum plant conditions for any species are, however, more difficult to predict. In practice, we are more concerned with populations than with individual requirements. In considering factors influencing population activity and size we have to consider those factors listed under "biotic" above and become involved in "synecology".

The interdependence of populations is best appreciated by studying a food cycle (*Fig.* 1.10) which represents the general food links between the major populations present in an aquatic environment. Within such

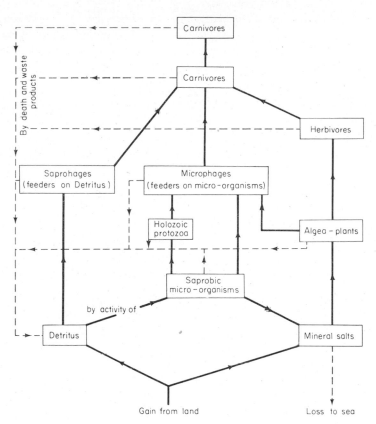

FIG. 1.10. A simplified representation of food cycles in streams.

a food cycle are several food chains in which successive links are represented by a series of different species which exist in a predator-prey relationship with neighbouring links. The number of links in such chains are usually few;

e.g. Diatom → Rotifer → Mayfly → Fish

The successive links of food chains are represented by fewer individuals, expressed by Elton (1935) as a pyramid of numbers (*Fig. 1.11*). Considering the pyramid as representing the different nutritional groups within a community, each horizontal section is known as a "trophic level". Thus organisms occupying the same trophic level are competing for a common food supply—a horizontal relationship. Those on successive levels are linked by a predator-prey relationship—

4*

a vertical relationship. These inter-relationships between populations result in a dynamic state of balance being established. Thus although theoretically all populations tend to increase at an intrinsic rate, they do, in fact, remain roughly constant, or fluctuate about a constant mean, for long periods.

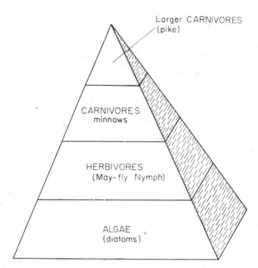

Fig. 1.11. Populations in a stream community represented as an Eltonian pyramid of numbers.

Processes by which populations are controlled have been divided into two types according to whether their controlling effect varies with the population density. Those, such as adverse climatic conditions and toxins, which result in a percentage kill independent of the size of the population, are said to operate as density-independent processes. Others, such as disease and food shortage, are more effective against dense populations than low ones and are termed density-dependent. Generally the environmental factors classified as physical and chemical previously, are usually density-independent whereas the biotic factors operate in a density-dependent manner. Although density-independent processes are capable of eliminating a population, the regulation of a population can only be effected by factors sensitive to the changes in the density of the population, i.e. density-dependent ones (Solomon, 1957).

The relative importance of density-dependent and density-independent processes in controlling populations is a matter of much controversy which is outside the scope of this work. The different views, strongly held, may in part be due to the different communities and environments on which the observations have been made. In this respect my own views, based on macrofauna population studies on bacteria beds, should be pertinent to our subject; they may be summarized as follows:

(i)   The physical and chemical factors of bacteria beds create a specialized habitat which few species have been able to colonize.

(ii)  Density-dependent factors, especially competition for the available food—the film of micro-organisms feeding on the organic waste—are most important in limiting populations at the high densities established by the few species which have successfully colonized the habitat.

(iii) The outcome of these density-dependent processes on the competing populations is, however, largely determined by physical factors such as the downward rate of flow of the liquid and the temperature.

(iv)  The effect of a physical factor operating through density-dependent biotic processes is greatly different in degree and sometimes the reverse of that to be expected if the physical factor acted directly on the population free from biotic pressure.

(v)   Slight changes in the physical environment may result in a change in the dominance of the competing species. Thus, seasonal fluctuations in temperature induce a succession of dominant species throughout the year, which in itself prevents the unlimited growth of any one population.

(vi)  Thus the macrofauna populations in bacteria beds are controlled by density-dependent biotic processes which are themselves monitored by physical factors.

The operation of waste-water treatment plants may be regarded as the controlling of the populations and activities of the different organisms present. Some knowledge of population dynamics is, therefore, desirable. Especially relevant are the growth curves of cultures of micro-organisms. A classical growth curve, as described by Monod

(1949) is shown in *Fig.* 1.12. The lag phase may be considered as a period of acclimatization which is followed by a phase of rapidly increasing growth rate leading to the log phase in which the maximum growth rate is achieved. This is terminated when, for reasons discussed

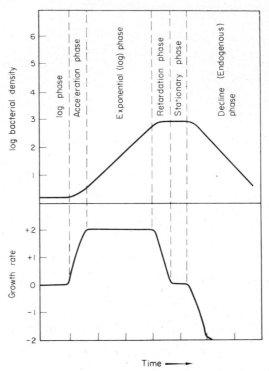

FIG. 1.12. Characteristic growth curves of cultures of microorganisms (After Mond., 1949). (Reproduced from Hawkes, H.A. (1961), an ecological approach to some bacteria bed problems, *J. Inst., Sewage Purif.* (2), by kind permission of the editor.)

later, the rate of cell division declines (the declining growth rate) until it is equalled by the rate of death of cells (the stationary phase) and eventually is exceeded by the latter resulting in a negative growth rate. The log phase of growth is terminated by adverse conditions such as depletion of nutrient requisites, accumulation of toxic by-products of metabolism or physical overcrowding, created by the activity of the micro-organisms themselves. Under starvation conditions the cells of the culture may undergo endogenous respiration using their own protoplasm as respiratory substrate. Within the colony, however, the viable cells may also utilize the breakdown products of the protoplasm of other dead cells; this is also considered as endogenous respiration and the phase of growth is now usually referred to as the endogenous phase.

If organisms in the log phase of growth are subjected to limiting nutrient concentrations—and a single nutrient factor may be limiting—

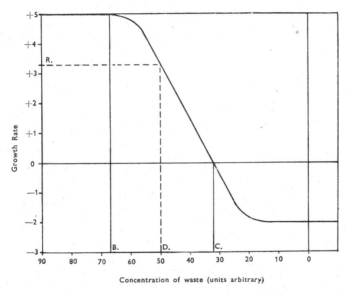

Concentration of waste (units arbitrary)

FIG. 1.13. Relationship between growth rate of microorganism and nutrient concentration. (Reproduced from Hawkes, H.A. (1961), An ecological approach to some bacteria bed problems, *J. Inst.*, *Sewage Purif.* (2), by kind permission of the editor).

the growth rate is reduced. This indeed is one of the causes terminating the exponential (log) phase of growth, but the organisms remain for some time capable of exponential growth when food is no longer limiting. The relationship between growth rate and food concentration is shown in *Fig.* 1.13. At high concentrations food is not limiting. Below a certain concentration (B) however, at which food becomes limiting, there is a successive reduction in the growth rate with decrease in nutrient concentration until the rate is zero at concentration (C) which is above 0 food concentration. Below this concentration (C) auto-oxidation (endogenous respiration) of the cells take place producing a negative growth rate. The concentrations at which these effects become operative differ with different organisms. In waste-water treatment plants it would appear that fungi require higher concentrations of nutrient than do bacteria and, therefore, with decreasing nutrient concentration it is possible that fungi pass into the declining growth phase and negative growth phase before bacteria.

## The Transfer of Materials and Energy between Populations

So far we have confined our discussion of the inter-relationships of populations to numbers. In studying the functional relationship, such as the transfer of materials and energy between populations, the amount of living matter—biomass—must be taken into account. Reconsidering the general food cycle (*Fig.* 1.10) in these terms, we see that the low energy inorganic matter is synthesized into high energy organic matter by the process of photosynthesis and protein synthesis by plants using light energy. This high energy material is used as food by a succession of organisms in a food chain, i.e. by organisms on successive trophic levels, either as predators or agents of decomposition. Each population, however, takes a 'cut' of the utilizable material it receives, this fraction is broken down in respiration to release energy for the life processes, the remainder is re-synthesized as the organism's protoplasm (biomass), to become available as food to the next link in the food chain or to the next trophic level. The end-products of the material broken down in respiration then become available for re-synthesis by plants, either directly in the case of C, H and O as $CO_2$ and $H_2O$ or indirectly in the case of protein respiration, via the nitrogen and phosphorus cycles. There is thus a reduction in calorific equivalent in successive trophic levels.

The proportion of the material (and energy) received by a population that is re-synthesized as biomass for use by populations in the next trophic level, varies with different organisms. In studies on the productivity of lakes in connection with fish production, the efficiency of a population is taken as the percentage of the calorific equivalent of food taken in that is made available to the next trophic level. This definition, however, reflects the interest of the final link in the food chain—man! Other organisms in the chain are not, however, primarily concerned with the production of biomass for use as food by their predators, but with their own life processes. A more objective definition of efficiency would be that percentage of the food energy which is used in the organism's life processes.

Which of these concepts of efficiency is more applicable to populations in waste water treatment plants depends upon the attitude one takes to the problem of waste treatment. In the past the problem has been regarded, by most workers involved in the practice of waste treatment, as one of disposal without causing pollution of the receiving water. The production of sludge from the mechanical settlement and biological oxidation of the waste is regarded as a secondary process. In some cases the resultant sludge may, after digestion, be used, e.g. as a fertilizer. Often, however, its disposal creates a major problem, especially at sites away from the coast where disposal at sea is not practicable. The production of sludge, especially the "secondary" sludges resulting from synthesis in biological oxidation, is not, therefore, generally desired. Accepting this concept of the aims of waste water treatment, the breakdown of as much as possible of the organic waste is preferable to its re-synthesis as biomass (sludge). On this concept, the efficiency of a population would be measured by the percentage of the material taken in by the population that is oxidized in the respiratory processes of the organisms.

An alternative concept of the role of waste water treatment lays stress on the conservation not only of the water but also of the valuable components of the waste. Hynes (1960), discussing what he describes as the appalling waste involved in the disposal of organic wastes, particularly sewage, calculated that each day the population of Great Britain wastes approximately 500 tons of saline nitrogen and 30 tons of phosphate phosphorus in sewage effluents alone. Although this may increase the fertility of the rivers, sometimes adversely affecting man's interests as when thick growths of blanket weed (*Cladophora*) occur, much of it passes to the ocean and is lost by the land and man. Of the total amount of phosphorus in the sewage arriving at a works, approximately a half passes away in solution in the effluent (Jenkins and Lockett, 1943). It has been estimated that about three quarters of the nitrogen is lost in this way (*Report of the Natural Resources Technical Committee*, 1954). The nitrogen and phosphorus retained in the sludge is partly from the primary settled sewage solids and partly from the secondary sludges formed in the biological oxidation plant. In digestion, however, there is a further loss as the organic nitrogen is broken down to soluble ammonium salts: these are usually returned to the oxidation plant in the sludge liquors, the ammonium concentration in which may be 700 ppm (amm. N). Thus the larger the proportion of the soluble organic waste that is synthesized as biomass (sludge), the less the loss of fertility. On this basis the efficiency of populations should be based on the percentage of the material received that is synthesized as biomass. This concept has also been expressed as the "economic co-efficient of cell synthesis" which may be considered as the ratio of dry weight of growth (biomass) to the corresponding weight of nutrient utilized. It has been shown (*Water Pollution Research* 1955) that this value was lower for zöogleal bacteria than for four species of fungi common in sewage treatment plants. Thus in oxidizing the same amount of sewage, more sludge would be produced when fungi were the dominant microbial organisms than when bacteria were.

In practice, however, the maximum synthesis of microbial mass in activated sludge plants and bacteria beds is not always compatible with efficient plant operation, as will be discussed later. In algal oxidation ponds where the breakdown products of the bacterial decomposition of the waste are re-synthesized by photosynthetic activity into algal cells (Isaac and Lodge, 1960), the policy of encouraging maximum synthesis could be applied. This method of treatment, however, depends on the presence of adequate periods of sunlight throughout the year and it is doubtful whether, under climatic conditions prevailing in the United Kingdom, algal ponds could prove à satisfactory alternative to bacteria beds and activated sludge. In high rate oxidation ponds in California, the algae have been harvested by alum flocculation or continuous centrifuging, and have been proved to be of value as a high-protein animal feed supplement (McGauhey, 1960). He considered it was not necessary to separate the algae from the bacterial cells, as both were high-energy compounds suitable for feeding stuff.

Attempts have been made to reclaim the nutrient salts from effluents of conventional plants by culturing rapidly growing crops in them. In South Africa experimental work has shown that the water-hyacinth *(Eichhornia crassipes)* could be used for such purposes (Howard, 1946), but again the lack of sunlight and the severity of winters in the United Kingdom make its use here impracticable. In countries where the nutrient matter in effluents can be recovered by the growth of plants, including algae, it is also possible to encourage further links in the food chain, such as invertebrate animals, on which fish can be success-fully cultured (Hey, 1955).

Ecologically the trapping of nutrients in effluents by plants is prob-ably limited in this country by the light energy available. Hynes (1960) has suggested that fertility might be recoverable in the form not of algae but sewage fungus, the development of which is independent of light. The direct re-use of effluents for irrigation purposes in America has been summarized by McGauhey, (1960). An alternative answer to this problem of conservation is illustrated in the direct application of certain industrial wastes to crops, e.g. gas liquor wastes (Pickering, 1958), cannery wastes (Dickinson, 1960). Such methods are similar in principle to the outmoded "sewage farms". In all such methods of conservation the public health aspect should, of course, be considered but this should not be confused with public prejudice against anything associated with sewage, which is common to the western civilization. In the direct application of waste to the land, care should also be taken to prevent the pollution of water courses via the land drains. Hynes (1960) stresses the need for some radical re-thinking of effluent disposal problems to develop practical methods of preventing this loss of fertility. However much one may agree with this view, the acceptance of any method of recovery, however technically feasible, is not in the hands of the chemist and biologist but will be decided by the accountant and economist. As long as "economy" is based on the arbitrary values of £. s. d., rather than on such intrinsic values as soil fertility, then it is feared that the declining fertility of the earth's soils will continue to be "poured down the drain" to be lost in the oceans.

*The Activity of Populations*

The rate at which organic matter is broken down is determined by the metabolic activity of a population, apart from its efficiency as described above. The metabolic rate, usually measured in terms of the rate of oxygen consumption per unit of biomass, differs considerably with different species. Generally this respiratory rate is more closely related to the surface area of the organism rather than to its weight, thus smaller organisms generally have a higher metabolic rate; e.g. the rate for the soil inhabiting Nematode worms is some ten times that of the larger earthworm (Overgaard, 1949). In assessing the relative importance of different species populations in a given community, it is not their numbers, nor their biomass, but their total metabolic activity that is important.

A concept of the activity of a community in terms of energy flow has been put forward by MacFadyen (1957). Although he himself warns us that the application of this concept to productivity studies had not yet been generally accepted, certain features would appear applicable to communities in waste water treatment plants. He points out that in food cycles, although materials recirculate, energy does not, the energy trapped in the plant during photosynthesis being liberated at different trophic levels by the heterotrophic organisms. The amount of energy entering a community depends upon the rate at which the materials are circulated. This depends not only on the photosynthetic activity of the plants but equally upon the rate at which energy is released by the heterotrophic organisms, thus providing nutrients for the plants. An active community is thus one in which there is a rapid liberation of energy. The relative importance of different populations within a community is then measured by their contribution to the energy flow of the community. A community which has a rich variety of species, able to exploit different energy sources, is a more productive community than one having few unspecialized species in which there may be "stagnant pools" of energy instead of a rapid flow. Although in waste-water treatment plants we are not primarily interested in productivity, the rate at which organic matter is broken down is of economic importance and this concept of energy flow could be applied to the community of organisms in the treatment plants.

*Application of Biological Principles*
*to Waste Water Treatment*

Of the three aspects of biology outlined in this introduction, both taxonomy and physiology are necessary for a full appreciation of ecology. For those desirous of further study of any of these aspects of biology a list of appropriate references is given at the end of this chapter. In applying biological principles to waste water treatment, involving the controlled activities of populations of organisms, the ecological approach is probably the most rewarding and will be developed in subsequent sections.

The different aspects of ecology are all reflected in the several studies of the organisms found in sewage-treatment plants. Some resulted in mere systematic lists of organisms associated with different stages of the process and which, although useful as a basis for other workers, are of no practical value to the operator. Other observers have correlated the presence of organisms with different conditions within the plant and such organisms have then been used as "indicator organisms". For example, early in the history of activated sludge, different associations of protozoa were associated with different levels of sludge efficiency (Ardern and Lockett, 1936) and microscopical examinations of the sludge to determine these associations were found to be of value in plant control. Probably because of the practical nature of the subject, early investigators enquired into the role of the different organisms in the purification process and thus the "synecological" aspect of the subject was introduced at an early stage. An outline of the historical development of our knowledge of the ecology of waste water treatment may be of interest.

*Historical Developments*
*in Waste Water Ecology*

The discovery that micro-organisms were associated with water and putrefying liquids was made possible by the invention in 1675 of the compound microscope by Leuwenhoek. It was not until 1743, however, that Baker indicated the scavenging activities of protozoa and bacteria, and in 1839 Schwann and Schultze demonstrated that micro-organisms were the true agents of decomposition (Johnson, 1914). Following his work, in the middle of the 19th century, on fermentation, Pasteur established the importance of micro-organisms in the process and distinguished between aerobic and anaerobic organisms for the first time. On the subject of organic wastes he declared "Dead matter which ferments and putrefies is not obedient, at any rate inclusively, to forces of a nature purely physical or chemical. It is life which rules over the work of death and the dissolution of animal and vegetable matter. This constant return to the atmospheric air and to the mineral kingdom of the constituents which vegetables and animals have borrowed from them is an act related to the development and multiplication of organized beings" (quoted Lockett, 1932).

The setting up of the River Pollution Commissions of 1865 and 1868, as a result of the foul conditions of the rivers of this country, first initiated a scientific study into the problems of sewage treatment. At that time, the recognized method of disposal was by land treatment, but there appears to have been no appreciation of the role of micro-organisms in the process in spite of the findings of earlier workers mentioned above. As a result of his investigations on the purification of sewage, Sir Edward Frankland in the second report of the Commission (1870) reported that the process was not merely mechanical filtration but involved chemical oxidation; the role of micro-organisms was apparently not appreciated. He did appreciate, however, the need for adequate aeration and as a result of his experiments he did devise the "intermittent filtration" method using land. It was truly claimed (Dunbar and Calvert, 1908) "that Frankland's conclusions, based as they were on excellent experiments, have formed the foundation for all further progress relating to sewage purification up to the present time" (1908). Unfortunately, however, his mechanical-chemical concept of the process has persisted, although in a subconscious form, and still influences the design and operation of biological treatment plants; the term sewage "filter" reflects this attitude to the process!

Later work, however, by Schloesing and Muntz (1877) showed that nitrification was brought about by micro-organisms and they concluded that these were essential to the purification process. Warington (1884) showed that nitrification proceeded in two stages, each stage being the result of the activity of separate organisms. These were later isolated as *Nitrosomonas* and *Nitrobacter* by Winogradsky (1890). For a more detailed history the reader is referred to Stanbridge (1954).

The role of larger animals in the stabilization of organic matter was also reported by Dr. Sorby to the Royal Commission on the Metropolitan Sewage Discharge in 1883. He associated the disappearance of sedimentary faecal matter in the river Thames with the presence of certain crustacea and worms. Thus before the advent of the bacteria bed, which was evolved from soil and sand filters as a result of experiments at the Lawrence Experiment Station, Massachusetts, the role of both the micro-organisms and the macrofauna in sewage purification had been established. The results of the Lawrence experiments stimulated investigations of the principles involved in the bacteria bed method of treatment. In these, although the role of the micro-organisms was appreciated by most, and studies were carried out on the bacterial flora, the activity of the larger organisms, previously associated with purification, was at first overlooked, their presence, when observed, being regarded as incidental, as indeed it still is by some workers.

Johnson (1914), in reviewing the early works, quoted Dunbar (1900) as first drawing attention to the function of higher animals and plants and states that later Höfer, in 1907, investigated their activities more closely. Dibdin in 1904 also observed the presence of large numbers of active insects and Annelid worms in his slate beds, and Fowler (1907) also reported on the importance of the higher forms of life in sewage purification. About the same time Harrison in his evidence to the Royal Commission on Sewage Disposal (1908) suggested that the seasonal discharge of solids from beds was probably due to the activity of the macrofauna. Work of a more truly ecological nature was carried out by Johnson (1914) when he studied the factors influencing the distribution of different species of macrofauna in bacteria beds at Wakefield. Parkinson and Bell (1919) demonstrated the useful activity of the springtail *Achorutes subviaticus* in controlling film accumulation.

Later, the environment of the bacteria bed, supporting a reduced number of species, attracted the attention of more academic workers as a habitat on which to study problems of the dynamics of populations. Notable among such workers were Dr. Lloyd and his succession of students at Leeds University who carried out a series of studies on insect and protozoan populations on sewage works in the West Riding; these are summarized by Lloyd (1945). Nuisance arising from flies leaving the bacteria beds probably attracted attention to the macrofauna before their beneficial activities were fully realized. (*Royal Commission on Sewage Disposal 5th Report* (1908) 119). Later, this nuisance resulted in many investigations into methods of control using different chemicals. Some such investigations were ecological in that they attempted to relate the populations to environmental conditions (Tomlinson and Stride, 1945) but most, although of practical value in assessing the effectiveness of different control measures, did not advance the knowledge of bacteria bed ecology. Another practical problem—the choking of the beds with accumulated film—has led to a series of ecological investigations both in this country (Reynoldson, 1941, 1942, 1948; Tomlinson, 1941, 1946; Hawkes, 1955, 1957, 1959) and in America (Heukelekian, 1945). At Birmingham a study on the effect of insecticide treatment on the bacteria bed community and film accumulation (Hawkes, 1955a) has led to the two practical difficulties being studied as one ecological problem.

In the ecology of activated sludge both academic interest and practical problems have initiated ecological investigations. Ecological successions of different species of protozoa in the development of a sludge and the relative roles of protozoa and bacteria in the process have been studied by many workers (see Barker, 1949). The development of filamentous growths associated with 'bulking' has also resulted in investigations being carried out (Ruchhoft and Watkins, 1928; Smit, 1934; Lackey and Wattie, 1940; Ruchhoft and Kachmar, 1941; Heukelekian, 1941).

The outcome of such ecological investigations usually results in the formulation of hypotheses which necessitate laboratory work for their proof or otherwise and much work being carried out at present by the Water Pollution Research Laboratory and others will, it is hoped, assist in the solution of outstanding ecological problems.

## Comparison of Activated-Sludge and Bacteria-Bed Environments

Before outlining the ecology of activated sludge and bacteria beds in the following two chapters let us first briefly compare their relative environments.

Although the treatment of waste waters by both methods involves similar biochemical processes the two differ in many respects. Firstly, whereas the activated sludge is truly an aquatic environment that of the bacteria bed has been likened to the wrack zone of the sea shore (Reynoldson, 1948). Also, whereas the fauna of activated sludge is normally restricted to microorganisms, the bacteria bed also supports higher forms of life such as oligochaete worms and insects. Associated with this difference in the fauna is the difference in the degree of control the operator has over the two biological systems. In the activated sludge process the amount of microbial mass is controlled by the withdrawal of excess sludge from the system; in the bacteria bed excess film is removed chiefly by biological agencies. These differences are shown diagramatically in *Fig.* 1.14.

A fundamental difference in the ecology of the two systems is that in the bacteria bed a succession of communities becomes established at different levels of the bed and associated with the corresponding different degrees of purification; whereas in the activated-sludge process the same community within the floc is at one time associated with the untreated waste and at the other extreme with the purified effluent.

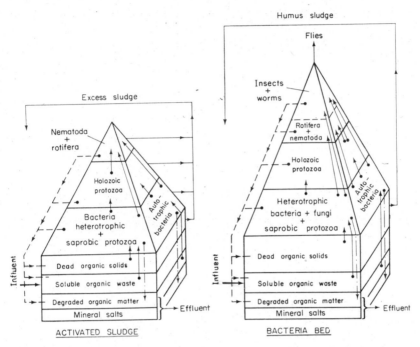

FIG. 1.14. Diagrammatic representation of the main food-links in the purification of organic wastes by activated sludge and by bacteria beds. (The full lines represent synthesis; the broken lines represent death and waste products; the chain-dotted lines represent by-products of respiraion).

It is of interest to note that many of the advantages and disadvantages of the two systems are attributable to these differences; fly nuisance and the choking of the beds being connected with film control by biological agencies; bulking of the sludge, with resultant settlement difficulties, and the difficulties associated with disposal of the surplus activated sludge are probably connected with its removal from the system as microbial flocs rather than as the faeces of the grazing fauna. Again, the relative sensitivity of activated sludge to toxic discharges may be associated with circulation of the sludge, whereas, in the more robust

5

bacteria beds such discharges are first taken by the surface growths. A highly nitrified effluent is more often associated with an efficient bacteria bed than with activated sludge and this may also be connected with the differences in the relative ecological systems. Nitrifying organisms are more effective in isolation from the other processes of purification, e.g. in the cleaner depths of the bacteria bed or in the cleaner secondary bed of the two-stage process. It may be therefore, that in the multipurpose floc of the activated sludge their activity is restricted. Also the length of life of a floc in the system is largely determined by the growth rate of the heterotrophic bacteria and may be such that the floc is discharged before the more slowly growing autotrophic nitrifying organisms become effectively established.

In nature, a succession of different ecological conditions and associated communities concerned with the breakdown of organic matter in waters has been described (Kolkwitz, 1950). A high concentration of complex decomposable organic matter is associated with the absence, or very low concentration, of oxygen—*Polysaprobic* condition. As purification proceeds and the organic matter is broken down first to amino-acids (*α-mesosaprobic*) and then to salts (*β-mesosaprobic*), the oxygen concentration increases until oxidation and mineralization is completed (*oligosaprobic*). Both the activated-sludge and the bacteria-bed environment differ from these systems in that, because of the aeration, high concentration of complex organic matter may be associated with fairly high oxygen concentrations.

Obviously large numbers of organisms gain access to both activated sludge plants and bacteria beds; many find the environment inhospitable and never become established; others may persist but are not very successful, whilst the few species which find the habitat suitable, increase greatly and with reduced competition may become more abundant than in their natural habitat. In the following discussion on the ecologies of the two processes only those organisms considered to have a significant role in the community, i.e. those organisms which if removed from the community would appreciably upset its balance of populations, are discussed.

## List of recommended books for further reading:

TAXONOMY
ALGAE
   WEST, G. S. and FRITSCH, F. E., *British Freshwater Algae*, C.U.P.
FUNGI
   GWYNNE-VAUGHAN, H.C.I. and BARNES, B., *Structure and Development of the Fungi* C.U.P.
   SMITH, G. *An Introduction to Industrial Mycology*, Edward Arnold (London) (1954).
BACTERIA
   BISSET, K. A. and MOORE, F. W. *Bacteria*, Livingstone, (Edinburgh).
   LAMANNA, C. and MALLETTE M. F. *Basic Bacteriology—Its Biological and Chemical Background*, Williams and Wilkins (Baltimore) (1953).
PROTOZOA
   KUDO, R.R. *Protozoology*, Charles C. Thomas (Springfield, Illinois).
INVERTEBRATES
   MACAN, T.T., *A Guide to Freshwater Invertebrate Animals*, Longmans. (London).
   BORRADAILE, L. A., EASTHAM, L.E.S., POTTS, F.A. and SAUNDERS, J.T. *The Invertebrata*, Third Ed. revised by Kerkut, G.A., C.U.P. (1958).
INSECTS
   IMMS, A.D., *A General Textbook of Entomology*, Methuen, (London).
PHYSIOLOGY
   YAPP, W.B. *An Introduction to Animal Physiology*, Clarendon Press, (Oxford).
   BALDWIN, E. *Dynamic Aspects of Biochemistry*, C.U.P. (1959).
ECOLOGY
   MACFAYDEN, A. *Animal Ecology*, Aims and Methods. Pitman (London) (1957).
   ANDREWARTHA, H.G. and BIRCH, L.C. *The Distribution and Abundance of Animals* (Chicago), (1954).


## Publications dealing specifically with biology of waste waters:

BARKER, A.N. (1949) Some microbiological aspects of sewage purification. *J. Inst. Sew. Purif.* (1) 7—22.

HYNES, H.B.N. *The Biology of Polluted Water*, U. P. (Liverpool) 1960.

JOHNSON, J.W.H. (1914) A contribution to the biology of sewage disposal. *J. Econ. Biol.* 9, 105—24; 127—64.

LIEBMANN, H. (1951) *Handbuch der Frischwasser- und Abwasserbiologie*, Vol. 1, R. Oldenbourg (München.)

LLOYD, Ll. (1945) Animal life in sewage purification processes. *J. Inst. Sew. Purif*, (2), 119—39.

SIMPSON, J.R. Some Aspects of the Biochemistry of Aerobic organic waste treatment, *Waste Treatment*. (Ed. ISAAC P.C.G.) Pergamon Press, Oxford, 1 – 30.

TOMLINSON, T.G. (1939) The biology of sewage purification. *J. Inst. Sew. Purif.* (1) 225—38.

*Animal life in percolating filters* (1946) Tech. Pap. Wat. Pollut. Res., Lond., No. 9, H.M. Stationery Office (London).

# CHAPTER 2

# THE ECOLOGY
# OF ACTIVATED SLUDGE

As mentioned previously, the environment of activated sludge can be regarded as an aquatic one. It is, however, unlike any natural aquatic habitat and although it has been colonized by numerous microorganisms, the constant agitation and recirculation of the sludge, make it inhospitable for aquatic macrofauna, which are rarely present. Bacteria, fungi, protozoa and the smaller metazoa such as rotifers and nematode worms are commonly found in activated sludges, though all may not be present in any one sludge.

Because of their need of light, algae, although they are introduced into the sludge with the sewage, rarely become established. Factors determining the dominant organisms in any sludge will be discussed later; first let us outline in more detail the more frequently occurring organisms in each of the above groups.

*Bacteria*

Bacteria can be regarded as the basis of the activated-sludge floc both structurally and functionally, and are universally present in the traditional activated sludge. Johnson (1914) was probably the first to report on the microorganisms in activated sludge and stated that 'zöoglea, assisted by other minute organisms chiefly of animal origin (protozoa) may be responsible for the rapid purification thus effected'. Russel and Bartow (1916) isolated thirteen varieties of non-nitrifying bacteria from activated sludge, most of which belonged to the *B. subtilis* group of aerobic spore-formers. The nitrifying bacteria *Nitrosomonas* and *Nitrobacter* were also isolated. These workers also demonstrated the importance of the non-nitrifying bacteria which they isolated in the purification of sewage. Buswell and Long (1923) as a result of microscopical examinations concluded that the sludge was composed of zöogleal masses intermixed with filamentous bacteria. Butterfield (1935) first isolated a zöoglea-forming bacterium from activated sludge. When aerated in sterile sewage a pure culture of this organism produced flocs similar to activated sludge and was found to be capable of removing a high percentage of the oxidizable material. This organism, identified as a variety of *"Zöoglea ramigera"*, was considered to be of importance in the process of purification; this was later confirmed by Butterfield and others (1937).

In an attempt to determine whether one species of zöogleal organism was present or whether there were several species prevalent, Heukelekian and Littman (1939) examined zöogleal bacteria from 15 different sludges and concluded that they were sufficiently alike to be classed either as one species or as one genus and were also indistinguishable from the zöogleal bacterium, *Zöoglea ramigera*, described by Butterfield (1935). These bacteria were Gram-negative, non-sporing, motile, capsulated rods. When aerated in sterile sewage they rapidly oxidized carbohydrates and produced ammonia from gelatin, casein and peptone, producing well-organized flocs; however, no nitrification took place. Other bacteria isolated by Heukelekian and Schulhoff (1938) were claimed to effect considerable clarification without producing a marked reduction in the oxygen consumption of the effluent when aerated with sewage. Generally, however, it became accepted that 'Z. ramigera', because of its ability to form flocs and to stabilize nutrient substrates, was the primary organism in activated sludge. Later work (McKinney and Horwood (1952), demonstrated that other organisms isolated from activated sludge were capable of floc formation when aerated in a suitable nutrient substrate. It has been suggested that all bacteria have, under certain environmental conditions, this ability to flocculate, this being determined by their relative surface-charges and energy-levels (McKinney, 1957). Once the floc has started to form some bacteria die and lyse, the insoluble polysaccharides remain in the floc and entrap the less active bacteria. Wooldridge and Standfast (1933) concluded that only a small proportion of the bacteria in sludge was living. Bacteria, however, although rendered incapable of active growth, are still able to carry out some chemical activity by unimpaired enzyme systems.

Bacteria entering the activated-sludge plant with the sewage are from two main sources, firstly those originally present in the water or in the infiltration water, and secondly, intestinal bacteria introduced with the faeces. Earlier workers found that the intestinal bacteria, particularly the *Bact. coli* and *Bact. aerogenes* group and the aerobic spore-forming bacteria predominated, and since many of these were found to be proteolytic, they concluded that the intestinal group of organisms played an important part in the purification of sewage. Allen (1944) however, using an homogenizer to disintegrate the flocs thereby isolating the bacteria within the floc and separating them from the smaller number of bacteria in the interstitial liquid, found that the intestinal bacteria were present in negligible numbers. By this method the counts were increased from ten- to one hundred-fold—counts of 2200 million/ml being recorded. The majority of strains isolated were Gram-negative rods with no action on carbohydrates, though many had decidedly proteolytic characteristics. The majority were members of the genera *Achromobacterium, Chromobacterium (Flavobacterium)* and *Pseudomonas.* He concluded that, because of their temperature relations and general characters and the fact that Taylor (1942) had found that the majority of bacteria from lakes and streams were Gram-negative rods as opposed to the dominant Gram-positive types in the soil, the bacteria which predominate in activated sludge are largely derived from water, intestinal forms being unimportant. The temperature of an activated-sludge plant would be expected to suit the aquatic types rather than the intestinal forms. Because of the different reported lists of species it is difficult to generalize on the dominant bacteria in activated sludge. Allen's list and that of the American workers, which included intestinal and non-intestinal forms have only *Flavobacterium* in common. The generally accepted '*Zöoglea ramigera*' was not included in Allen's list and it may be that it is not a true species but a growth form of various species. Allen's isolation technique by homogenization would be expected to reveal the dominant species, although on the other hand, the American workers demonstrated that their species were capable of floc formation.

Apart from the zöoglea-forming bacteria mentioned above, filamentous bacteria are also found. Because of their association with the condition known as bulking when the sludge becomes difficult to settle, much attention has been paid to these growths. Unfortunately the identification of the organisms is in some cases open to question.

However, *Sphaerotilus natans* is probably the most common filamentous bacterium in activated sludge.Lackey and Wattie (1940) isolated fourteen strains of *Sphaerotilus* from different sources and in culture these behaved so similarly that they concluded they were all *Sphaerotilus natans*

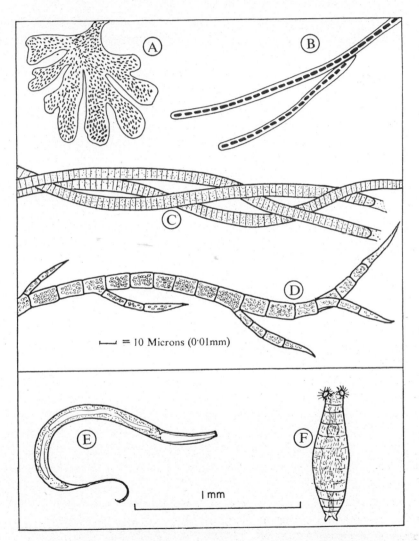

⌐⌐ = 10 Microns (0·01mm)

l mm

FIG. 2.1. Some micro-organisms of activated sludge and bacteria beds: (A) *Zooglea ramigera*, (B) *Sphaerotilus natans*, (C) *Phormidium* sp., (D) *Stigeoclonium*, (E) a nematode worm, (F) a rotifer.

Kutzing and that this was capable of variation according to environment. This view is supported by the more recent report by Pringsheim (1949) that the different filamentous forms previously known as *Sphaerotilus, Leptothrix* and *Cladothrix* are in fact different growth forms of one identical organism. In view of this it is probable that *Sphaerotilus natans* is the most common filamentous bacterial form in activated sludge. Other forms however, besides those now known to be *Sphaerotilus,* have been found. Lackey and Wattie in their work on *Sphaerotilus* frequently isolated a similar form which they tentatively identified as *Bacillus mycoides* and which had different cultural characteristics. Ruchhoft and Watkins (1928) isolated a filamentous bacteria from activated sludge. They described it as consisting of disc-shaped cells $2-3\mu$ each in diameter and $2-4\mu$ long, lying within a barely perceptible sheath in straight unbranched chains $1000-5000\mu$ long. It differed from *Sphaerotilus* in showing no branching and did not produce conidia.

Smit (1934) also concluded that other filamentous growths found in bulking activated sludge did not agree with the description of *Sphaerotilus*. Besides these unidentified forms, *Crenothrix* and *Beggiatoa* have also been reported (Taylor, 1930; Buswell, 1931).

*Fungi*

Although common in bacteria beds, fungi are relatively rare in activated sludge; at least, reference to the literature reveals few reports of their presence. Smit (1934) in studies on filamentous bacterial growths in activated sludge also found a fungus identified as a species of the genus *Geotrichoides*, which he named *G. paludosus*. He considered however that this was not the cause of the bulking of the sludge. When present, fungi may dominate the sludge under abnormal circumstances. In work on the oxidation of lactose by activated sludge (Jenkins and Wilkinson, 1940) the dominant organism of the sludge was found by Tomlinson to be the fungus *Pullularia pullulans*. In the same investigations Tomlinson also isolated species of the following fungi from the activated sludge: *Phoma, Oospora* and *Sporotrichum*. The activated sludge in a pre-treatment plant at Yardley, Birmingham, is frequently dominated by growths of *Öospora (Geotrichum)* sometimes to the exclusion of the bacterial floc.

*Protozoa*

The presence of protozoa in activated sludge has always aroused much interest and conjecture as to their role in the process. Johnson (1914) was, again, probably first to report their presence; since then numerous workers have listed different genera from plants operating under different conditions: Richards and Sawyer (1922), Buswell and Long (1923), Kolkwitz (1926), Ardern and Lockett (1936), Agersborg and Hatfield (1929), Taylor (1930) and Barker (1949). As discussed later the ciliates are the most common class in an efficient sludge, but to include the different conditions of sludges the more commonly listed genera of each class are given in *Table* 2.1.

*Metazoa*

Of the highe rforms of life rotifers and nematode worms are occasionally found and at times they may become so abundant as to be considered a factor in the ecological system. In few plants, however, can they be regarded as permanent members of the community. Other higher forms are of even rarer occurrence, *Cyclops,* the worm *Aelosoma* and chironomid larvae of the *Thummi* group being reported from isolated plants.

INTERRELATIONSHIPS OF THE DIFFERENT
POPULATIONS IN THE SLUDGE COMMUNITY
AND THEIR ENVIRONMENT

In waste treatment involving the breakdown of organic matter the saprobic forms are the primary feeders and primary agents of purification, although, as we shall see, holozoic animals also play an important secondary role. In the activated sludge and in the film of bacteria beds heterotrophic bacteria, saprophytic fungi and saprobic protozoa are the primary feeders occupying the basic trophic level. Holozoic protozoa occupy successively higher levels, the apex possibly being represented by the nematodes and rotifers (*Fig.* 1.14).

Of the three classes of protozoa represented in the activated sludge the rhizopoda engulf food particles within the pseudopodia by which they move. Soluble foods may also be absorbed, however, so they must

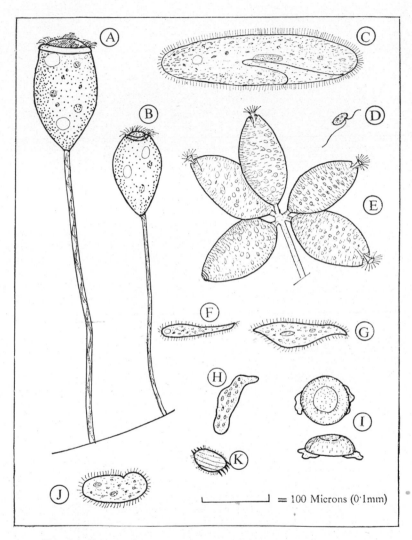

FIG. 2.2. Some protozoa common in activated sludge and bacteria beds: (A) *Vorticella sp.*, (B) *Vorticella microstoma*, (C) *Paramoecium candatum*, (D) *Bodo candatus*, (E) *Opercularia* sp., (F) *Lionotus fasciola*, (G) *Amphileptus* sp., (H) *Amoeba limax*, (I) *Arcella vulgaris* (surface and side views), (J) *Colpidium colpoda*, (K) *Aspidisca polystyla*.

TABLE 2.1 SOME SPECIES OF PROTOZOA COMMONLY RECORDED IN ACTIVATED SLUDGE

| RHIZOPODA Move and ingest food by pseudopodia (Mobile protoplasm) | FLAGELLATA Move by flagella (Whip-like processes) | CILIOPHORA Move by Cilia (Hair-like processes) | | |
|---|---|---|---|---|
| | | Free-Swimming | Crawling on sludge floc | Stalked |
| Amoeba sp. | Bodo caudatus | Paramoecium caudatum | Aspidisca sp. | Acineta sp. |
| Amoeba actinophora | Cercobodo longicauda | Paramoecium sp. | Euplotes sp. | Podophrya fixa |
| Arcella vulgaris | Monas sp. | Colpidium colpoda | Oxytricha fallax | Vorticella spp. |
| Actinophrys sp. | Oikomonas termo | Amphileptus spp. | Stylonychia sp. | Opercularia sp. |
| Vahlkampfia limax | Euglena sp. | Lionotus fasciola | | Epistylis plicatilis |
| V. guttula | Cercomonas sp. | Chilodon sp. | | Carchesium sp. |
| | Pleuromonas jaculans | Trichoda pura | | |
| | Anthophysa vegetans | Loxophyllum sp. | | |
| | Peranema sp. | | | |

be considered as both holozoic and saprophytic. The flagellates which move by one or more whip-like flagella may either be autotrophic (the pigment-bearing phytoflagellates, e.g. *Euglena*), saprobic, e.g. *Cercobodo*, or holozoic, e.g. *Oikomonas*. The ciliophora, which move by fine hair-like processes (cilia), are represented in activated sludge mostly by holozoic species although, again, some of these may also be capable of saprozoic nutrition.

Factors determining the population of any species are the intrinsic rate of increase, the availability of food in competition with other species on the same trophic level and the predatory effect of larger organisms. Apart from these "biotic" factors the environment of an organism is also affected by physical and chemical factors. In activated sludge the availability of oxygen, the pH, temperature, inhibitory agents, either toxic or antibiotic, and the physical turbulence of the process are probably the chief factors to be considered. Many different species are introduced with the sewage into the activated sludge; many find the environment unsuitable and either die out or fail to increase; others, suited to the environment, persist.

Of those on the same trophic level, competing for the same food, one becomes dominant, depending upon the relative rates of increase. According to "Gause's theorem" this situation should lead to the elimination of the other competing species, but this does not happen in activated sludge probably because the changing conditions, as the sludge passes through the system, successively favour different species, and the constant introduction of a mixed flora maintains the competition for food. The food of the primary feeders, the saprobic types, is the organic matter in the sewage. Thus many bacteria and fungi and the saprobic protozoa are in direct competition for this basic food supply. Others with different organic food requirements such as the autotrophic bacteria requiring less-complex nitrogen sources, are not in competition with these for food although in the same environment; they may, however, be competing for oxygen if that is limiting. The holozoic forms are predatory on the saprobic forms or on other holozoic forms and are therefore in the secondary or higher trophic levels. Competition may exist between these if they are dependent upon a common prey.

There is also the relationship between predator and prey to be considered. The population of the predator species is determined by the numbers of prey, an increase in the population of the prey is followed by an increase in the predator population which results in a decrease in the prey and in turn in a decrease in predator; thus fluctuating populations occur. This system is influenced by the extent to which the prey can seek refuge from the predator; in activated sludge the floc is probably of ecological significance in this respect. Holozoic forms by their predatory nature actively control the population in lower trophic levels, but the control effected by the saprobic organisms as prey, is a passive one.

Activated sludge may, then, be regarded as a complex ecological system, the organisms of which exist at different trophic levels, in each of which competition for common foods exists and between which there is a series of predator-prey relationships. Thus different populations exist, some dependent on, and some independent of, each other. Superimposed on these biotic forces are the physical and chemical factors of the environment mentioned before. These factors operate on the balanced community and their effects are not readily measurable in terms of their isolated effects on the individual members of the community as determined in pure-culture work; their differential effect on the different organisms is sometimes more important than their direct effect. In any such system the dominant organism of those in competition at any trophic level for a common food will be that which, under the conditions prevailing, is able to multiply most rapidly on the available food; this is largely determined by the relative size of the organisms and by their metabolic rate. It has, however, been suggested that in assessing the importance of species population in a community, biomass is more useful than numbers and that the sum metabolic activity of the population is of even greater value (Macfadyen, 1957). In a study of the role of organisms in the process of sewage purification, the sum of the metabolic activities of the different populations would be of greater value than would numbers or biomass, but unfortunately most of the ecological work up to date on sewage plants has been on populations. On the basis of these general principles we shall now examine the findings of different workers on activated-sludge ecology.

## FACTORS DETERMINING THE CHARACTER AND DOMINANT ORGANISMS OF A SLUDGE

Although algae, bacteria, fungi and protozoa are introduced into the activated sludge, in the majority of cases investigated, bacteria become dominant as primary feeders on the organic waste, different holozoic protozoa occupying the secondary trophic level with possibly rotifers and nematode worms at higher levels in the food chain. Algae, because of their need of light, are rarely present; fungi may predominate as primary feeders under abnormal circumstances to be discussed later.

Firstly the bacterial and protozoan populations will be considered. The dominant bacteria of the sludge must satisfy two conditions: they must be able to utilize the organic waste and also be capable of readily forming flocs to facilitate separation from the effluent, and thereby to ensure their retention in the system. The American workers demonstrated these capabilities for the species that they isolated from sludges treating sewage. The oxidation of strong non-toxic organic wastes by non-flocculent growths, involving the aeration of a soil suspension of the organisms with the waste, has been demonstrated by Heukelekian (1949). No separation of the organisms by settlement is attempted and the effluents although greatly reduced in strength are turbid. This process is being developed as a pretreatment process for organic wastes, but for the purpose of this paper is not included as an activated-sludge process.

For the successive stages in the complete oxidation and mineralization of complex organic wastes in sewage a number of different bacteria, not in direct competition, would be present. From reports it would appear that one or few heterotrophic bacteria are involved in the initial stages of sewage purification, the autotrophic bacteria *Nitrosomonas* and *Nitrobacter* completing the process. These later stages have not been closely studied in the U.S.A., probably owing to lack of interest in that country in taking purification to the stage of nitrification. Unlike the bacteria bed, where these successive stages are carried out by the respective organisms developed at different levels in the bed, all the bacteria in the activated-sludge system usually occupy the same physical niche, i.e. the floc, and, although not in direct competition for food, probably compete for oxygen. Nitrifying organisms are the most sensitive to inadequate aeration and it may be that the greater difficulty in obtaining a nitrified effluent with activated sludge than with the bacteria bed is due to this ecological difference in the two systems.

The dominant bacteria will be determined largely by the nature of the waste being treated. Engelbrecht and McKinney (1957) found, by developing sludges on a range of organic compounds, that sludges developed on structurally related compounds have similar morphological appearances and produce similar biochemical changes, whilst those developed from compounds morphologically different were structurally different. The pentose sugars, xylose and arabinose produce similar dense flocs, but a floc dominated by large filamentous types is developed on the hexose sugars, glucose and fructose. Because of their assocation with bulking sludge, much attention has been paid to factors encouraging the filamentous bacteria such as *Sphaerotilus*. Reports of conditions under which *Sphaerotilus* will develop are somewhat at variance, especially in relation to its oxygen requirements. That certain compounds especially carbohydrates, encourage its developement is well-known; in streams its growth is stimulated by trade-effluent discharges from the manufacture of beet sugar, paper, rayon, glue and flour, as well as textile bleach, coke by-products, dairy wastes and spent sulphite liquors (Harrison and Heukelekian, 1958). Available carbohydrates are not of frequent occurrence in sewages and the frequency of *Sphaerotilus* growths would suggest that other nutrients or other causes are responsible. Apart from this nutritional effect the degree of availability of oxygen may also be important. Several workers have associated the presence of *Sphaerotilus* with inadequate aeration and although some workers consider it an obligate aerobe like the zöogleal bacteria (Ruchhoft and Kachmar, 1941), others describe it as being able to withstand a considerable degree of deoxygenation.

Ingold (1940) concluded that it was a facultative anaerobe and that it grew more rapidly as the oxygen was depleted. In polluted streams, although this organism is rare in anaerobic conditions, profuse growths are found in water low in oxygen as well as in well-aerated, organically enriched waters. It would appear therefore that although *Sphaerotilus* may grow better at higher oxygen concentrations as reported, some strains at least are able to withstand fairly low oxygen concentrations—probably more so than the competing zöogleal forms—in which case the growth of filamentous forms growing in competition with zöogleal bacteria would be encouraged by lower oxygen concentrations. The relation between these filamentous growths and bulking is discussed later.

The nature of the bacterial flora of primary feeders is then determined chiefly by the nature of the food, i.e. the organic waste, and secondly by the conditions within the plant, chiefly the degree of aeration. Allen (1944) found that a succession of dominant bacteria occurred during the development of an efficient sludge, the predominant flora changing from a non-proteolytic to a proteolytic one. This he explained by suggesting that by aerating sewage, in which the carbohydrate and protein content is relatively small, bacteria suited to such dilute fluids would first develop producing the floc; as this builds up, sufficient protein becomes available in the floc to encourage the proteolytic forms; carbohydrates, however, are still sparse and hence the absence of the saccharolytic species. Similar successions have been observed for the protozoa (Barker 1949) and these may also be explained for the most part, although not entirely, by nutritional changes. The general succession in which a fauna dominated by rhizopods and flagellates is replaced first by the free-swimming ciliates and later by the attached peritrichous forms as the sludge becomes more efficient, is shown diagramatically in *Fig.* 2.3.

It must be stressed, however, that this is a general picture and that there are several exceptions, some species of *Amoeba* and *Arcella* in the rhizopoda for example, are more often associated with a more efficient sludge. Availability of requisite food, oxygen requirements, relative energy requirements and habit (i.e. whether free-swimming, crawlers, or attached) are all factors to be considered in accounting for such successions. Unfortunately our knowledge of such factors, especially nutritional, is far from complete. Initially, however, in the sewage, from which the sludge is developed, both soluble and suspended particulate organic matter is present; the primary feeders, heterotrophic bacteria and saprobic protozoa, mostly rhizopods and flagellates, will compete for food. As the bacteria increase in numbers secondary feeders become established. The holozoic flagellates will appear first because of their lower energy requirements. Later these are replaced by the holozoic ciliates with a more efficient feeding mechanism. Within the ciliates themselves there is a succession of species; the attached peritrichous forms having a lower energy level, replace a dominance of free-swimming forms as their common food becomes limited with increased purification.

Because of food preferences different species of holozoic ciliates would be expected to occur in association with the succession of domi-

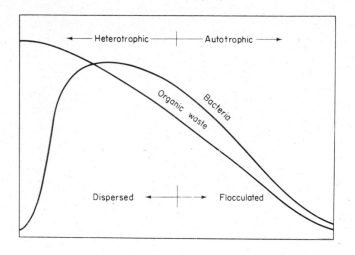

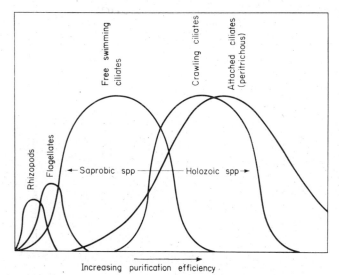

FIG. 2.3. Hypothetical curves showing successions of dominant protozoa in relation to the degree of purification of organic waste and bacterial population.

nant bacteria. Gray (1952) found that the ciliate fauna of a Cambridge-shire chalk stream was determined by the bacterial flora, *Paramoecium* and *Colpoda* being associated with the abundance of Gram-negative rods. Further stages of purification, not usually achieved in the plant, would result in the development of autotrophic algae, such as diatoms, and these in turn would support the larger species of holozoic ciliates. This succession, although primarily determined by nutritional require-ments, is also affected by the degree of tolerance to oxygen deficiency, the saprobic species generally being more tolerant. The degree of floc-culation of the bacteria may also be important. In early stages of sludge development the bacteria are dispersed in the liquid and this encourag-es the truly free-swimming forms; as the bacteria become flocculated however, the attached forms and those which browse on the flocs become dominant (Horasawa, 1949). In some sludges a third trophic level is represented by rotifers and nematodes which feed on the holo-zoic protozoa, although some possibly may feed on bacteria and other primary feeders. These are usually associated with higher degrees of purification. The occasional invasion of the sludge by chironomid larvae must be considered as the introduction of such a trophic level, although in practice it is reported that they destroy the effectiveness of the sludge floc.

Because of the recirculation of the sludge such successions do not occur in the activated-sludge process, but the protozoan fauna can be considered as being determined by the average stage of purification in the plant, being affected both by the strength of the incoming sewage and by the quality of the effluent. The presence of certain protozoa in an efficient sludge does not necessarily prove that they play an impor-tant role in the purification process; they may merely reflect the satis-factory conditions prevailing. The relative roles of bacteria and proto-zoa in the process have been variously assessed. Butterfield and Wattie (1941) found that efficient purification could be achieved by protozoa-free zöoglea; on the other hand, Pillai and Subrahmanyan (1944) reported that pure cultures of the ciliate *Epistylis* were capable of effective purification and considered bacteria of secondary importance.

To play the primary role of purification, however, the protozoa concerned must act as primary feeders in the ecological system. Al-though, as outlined, some saprobic protozoa, especially the rhizopods and flagellates, do compete with bacteria at this level, the bacteria are nearly always dominant and in an efficient sludge such protozoa are rare.

It has been suggested that holozoic ciliates normally feeding on bacteria may also be capable of saprophytic nutrition. Even if this is so it is doubtful whether such facultative saprophytes could compete with the obligate saprophytic bacteria and it is therefore reasonable to conclude that the primary agents of purification are the bacteria. The relative importance of the protozoa, however, even if a secondary role, is difficult to establish. Several workers have demonstrated that different protozoa are capable of agglutinating bacteria:

*Epistylis* and to less extent *Vorticella* (Pillai and Subrahmanyan, 1942)

*Balantiophorus minutus* (Watson, 1943)

*Oikomonas termo* (Hardin, 1943)

*Paramoecium caudatum* (Barker, 1946).

Sugden and Lloyd (1950) also demonstrated the ability of the ciliate *Carchesium* to clarify turbid waters. The extent to which this capacity is effective in the activated-sludge process is difficult to assess. Jenkins (1942) considered that although flocculation was important in purification, it was not dependent upon protozoa. By suppressing the protozoa in an activated sludge several workers attempted to assess their importance. In most cases the reduction in protozoa coincided with a more turbid effluent of high B.O.D. but these results may have been brought about by the effect of the suppressant on the bacterial floc. The resultant improvement in efficiency of a bacterial sludge after adding protozoa is, however, more positive evidence. Butterfield (1935) added the ciliate *Colpidium* to pure cultures of 'Zöoglea ramigera' and this resulted in a more efficient system.

More recently McKinney and Gram (1956) in experiments designed to demonstrate competition and predator-prey relationships in activated sludge, found that although pure cultures of bacteria formed typical flocs in nutrient solutions, some active bacteria remained free, producing turbidity and contributing to the B.O.D. of the effluent. When holophytic flagellates were added to such cultures they rapidly died off in competition with the bacteria although they were able to live on the nutrient alone. On adding the holozoic ciliates *Tetrahymena* and *Glaucoma scintillans*, however, these rapidly increased in numbers feeding on the free bacteria; because of the refuge of the floc, however, the bacteria were not eliminated and a balance was established. The result-

6*

ant effluent was less turbid and the B.O.D. was reduced. It would thus appear that protozoa can play an important role in the production of highly clarified effluents.

Apart from enhancing purification by flocculation holozoic protozoa may also act as population stimulators. In culture work it has been shown that bacterial activity may be increased by the predatory activity of protozoa: Cutler and Bal (1926) showed that rate of nitrogen fixation by the bacteria *Azotobacter* was increased by the presence of protozoa; Meiklejohn (1932) showed a similar effect by the ciliate *Colpidium* on the breakdown of proteins to ammonia. By their predatory activity it was assumed that they maintained the bacterial culture in the active log-phase of growth. Recently however McKinney (1957) distinguished between the log-phase, in which the total metabolic activity and the synthesis of microbial material increased rapidly, and the following phase of declining growth, leading to a phase in which oxidation of the waste is continued, to produce energy for life of the organisms, but in which no synthesis of microbial material takes place. At first sight it would appear that the more active log-phase should be maintained within the plant, but although oxidation is more rapid, little flocculation of the bacteria occurs and a higher proportion of the waste is converted into sludge which requires further treatment. In the later stage, although purification is slower, excellent flocculation occurs and no sludge accumulates, but because all the waste is oxidized and none synthesized as microbial material, more oxygen is required and the time of retention, therefore, has to be increased. To what extent these different phases of growth found in cultures can be applied to an activated-sludge plant, is open to question; McKinney (1957), however, considered that most plants operate between the declining growth and the later 'endogenous' phase.

We now turn to the fungi and their occurrence in activated sludge plant. The saprophytic fungi are in competition with the other primary feeders, chiefly the bacteria, and since with domestic sewage the conditions appear to favour bacteria, the fungi do not become established in the sludge. Under exceptional circumstances, however, usually associated with the treatment of trade wastes, fungi may become dominant. Some factors in industrial wastes causing this have been enumerated by McKinney (1957) as:

1. low oxygen caused by excessive organic loading or under-aeration and resulting in acid conditions from incomplete oxidation;
2. low pH which usually favours fungal growth;
3. low nitrogen, fungi requiring less nitrogen per unit mass of protoplasm than bacteria.

At the Yardley Works (Birmingham) the occurrence of *Öospora* is associated with acid flushes of trade wastes. In laboratory experiments at Birmingham on the treatment of phenolic wastes Harkness (unpublished results) found that a non-filamentous sludge was developed, but an accidental introduction of an acid sample of the waste resulted in filamentous growths of *Öospora* developing within two days.

Of ecological interest is the recent report (Cooke and Ludzack, 1958) of the effect of a predatory fungus, *Zöophagus insidians*, which invaded several laboratory activated-sludge units. The decreased efficiency of the sludge in removing nitriles was attributed to the predatory activity of the fungus in limiting the numbers of the rotifers which, it was considered, were the principal predators controlling the bacterial population.

Besides probably causing bulking it has been shown that the 'economic coefficients of cell synthesis', determined experimentally as the ratio of dry weight of growth to the corresponding weight of glucose destroyed, was much lower for two zöogleal bacteria than for four species of fungi examined (*Water Pollution Research* 1955). Thus at the same efficiency more sludge would be produced when fungi became the dominant primary feeder of the sludge.

*Bulking of Activated Sludge*

The condition known as bulking occurs when the sludge becomes difficult to settle and this usually results in an inferior effluent due to the amount of sludge which it contains. This may result from a number of causes, but is usually associated with the development of filamentous growths of bacteria such as *Sphaerotilus* or fungi. Most workers consider that such filamentous organisms are the causative organisms. Under laboratory conditions a pure bacterial culture sludge could not be induced to bulk even when conditions favoured bulking (Littman, 1940). Ruchhoft and Kachmar (1941) however considered that even when *Sphaerotilus* was present at times of bulking it was not the primary cause although its presence accentuated the condition. Bulking may occur in the absence of bacterial filamentous growths; Pillai and Subrahmanyan (1942–3) reported that it could be brought about by the death, and subsequent bacterial attack on colonies, of *Epistylis* (an attached ciliate) when aeration was inadequate.

At Birmingham the fungus *Geotrichum* is considered to be the responsible organism for bulking in a partial activated-sludge plant treating industrial sewage. It should be noted, however, that a bulking sludge although difficult to settle may by quite efficient in purifying the waste, probably because of the open nature of the floc. Whatever the mechanism of bulking, the result can be described as a biophysical response to an upset of the ecological balance. Oxygen, food supply and toxicity are probably the chief factors which cause such upsets to occur. It is necessary to distinguish between acute bulking, brought on suddenly by toxic discharges, and chronic bulking which results from adverse conditions within the plant (Heukelekian, 1941).

# CHAPTER 3

# THE ECOLOGY
# OF BACTERIA BEDS

THE artificial environment of a sewage bacteria bed has been successfully invaded by truly aquatic micro-organisms and some moisture-
loving higher organisms, and it is convenient to distinguish between
the micro-organisms or 'film' and the higher forms of life, the grazers,
although as will be appreciated, some organisms of the film are also
grazers in the strictest sense.

## ORGANISMS OF THE FILM

*Bacteria*

Bacteria active in bacteria beds have attracted little attention; according to Wattie (1943) bacteria found in filter slimes are zöogleal bacteria
of one group closely related to those in activated sludge. Besides zöogleal bacteria, filamentous forms such as *Sphaerotilus* and *Beggiatoa* are
also present, but since they have not been associated with nuisance
such as bulking in activated sludge, their occurrence has not been
studied in the same detail.

The nature of the bacteria flora will be determined by the nature of
the waste. Happold and Key (1932) showed that after the application
of gas liquor to a bed the bacterial flora underwent considerable modification, bacteria capable of utilizing certain components of gas liquor
becoming established. Specific bacteria capable of oxidizing phenols,
and thiocyanates, thiosulphates and cyanides have been isolated. Fourteen well-defined pure organisms were isolated by Harrison from the
Monsanto plant treating the trade effluent containing a number of
organic compounds; some were found to be specific over the range
of compounds tested, whilst others attacked several compounds (Wilson

1954). One would expect different bacteria associated with different stages of breakdown to be established at different levels of the bed, the heterotrophic forms being nearer the surface and the autotrophic ones nearer the base of the bed. Although samples of waste taken at different depths suggest that this is so (Mills, 1945), there appears to have been little work done on the actual distribution of organisms. Barritt (1933) measured the nitrite produced by inoculating sterile solutions containing ammonium salts with effluent from different levels of his sectional bed. He concluded from his results that nitrifying organisms occur in all sections of the bed, but on the basis of the higher nitrite yield by the inoculum from the lower sections, it could be considered that they were more common in the lower portions of the bed. Using samples of the film removed from different levels in connection with film-accumulation studies, Harkness compared their relative nitrifying capacities and found that although nitrate production was highest in the lower samples, nitrite production was more evenly distributed throughout the different depths, indicating a concentration of nitrate-producing bacteria near the base of the bed, with the nitrite-producers distributed throughout the depth. It should be mentioned that the bed from which the sample was removed was operating on alternating double filtration.

*Fungi*

Fungi are of more common occurrence in bacteria beds than in activated sludge. This may be because of the more suitable physical environment or may be because of the constant supply of complex organic matter at or near the surface of the bed; in an efficient activated sludge they would be subjected to starvation conditions for considerable periods. As saprophytes and primary feeders they are in direct competition with the heterotrophic bacteria and it would appear that the nature and stage of purification of the waste determines which is dominant at the different levels of the bed. With domestic sewage, bacteria usually predominate, but with the introduction of trade wastes, fungi may become dominant especially in the upper part of the bed (Hawkes, 1957). Numerous fungi have been isolated from beds but probably the following are the more important ecologically, although other species may be dominant locally under certain conditions: *Fusarium aqueductum*, *Öospora* (*Geotrichum*), *Sepedonium* sp.,

*Ascoidea rubescens, Subbaromyces splendens, Sporotrichum* sp., *Penicillium* sp. It is of interest to note that the commonly occurring truly aquatic *Leptomitus lacteus* does not generally appear to have colonized the bac-

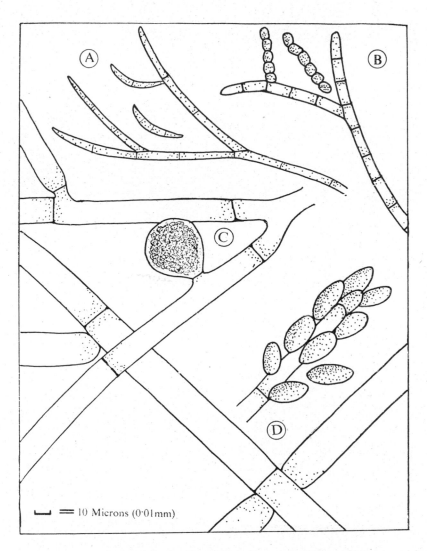

FIG. 3.1. Some bacteria-bed fungi showing characteristic spores.
(A) *Fusarium aqueductum*, (B) *Geotrichum* sp., (C) *Sepedonium* sp.,
(D) *Ascoidea rubescens*.

teria-bed environment. At one works, although it was found in the feed channels in profuse growths and when detached, blocked the distributor arms, it did not establish itself within the beds. It would appear that the physical environment of the bed determines the species which can inhabit it. Those with tenacious holdfasts such as *Fusarium* and *Geotrichum* are the first to colonize the stones and form a basis for the subsequent establishment of such form, as *Sepedonium* and *Ascoidea*. Painter (1954) considered that the different growth-rates and nitrogen requirements of *Fusarium* and *Sepedonium* also contributed to this succession. Tomlinson (1942) found that although *Fusarium* and *Geotrichum* (*Öospora*) were able to withstand the direct discharge of sewage, *Fusarium* was dominant on the surface and *Geotrichum* below; factors other than the structural modifications mentioned above were obviously involved. As a result of experiments in which growths were developed in light and dark he found that *Fusarium* was able to compete successfully with the algae *Stigeoclonium* and *Chlorella* in the presence of light, while *Geotrichum* was unable to do so. In the absence of algae (in the dark) *Geotrichum* competed successfully with *Fusarium* and became the dominant fungus. Thus the dominance of *Fusarium* on the surface of the bed was due to its ability to compete successfully with the algae. He considered that algae might thus limit the growths of fungi on the surface of beds, *Geotrichum* producing thicker mats than *Fusarium*.

On the surface of the beds at Birmingham, served by fixed spray jets, a seasonal succession of dominant species has been observed, the bacterial zöogleal growth of the summer giving way to *Fusarium* which later became overgrown by *Geotrichum* and later, following incipient ponding, by thick growths of *Sepedonium*. The foam-like growths of *Ascoidea* are usually found within the bed. On beds served with travelling distributors, under the jets of which the sewage impinged on the surface with considerable force, only *Fusarium* and *Geotrichum* became established under jets but as these growths impeded the flow and the sewage spread laterally to the areas between the jets, *Sepedonium* and *Ascoidea* became established in these zones. Factors influencing the amount of fungal growths in beds will be discussed in detail later.

*Algae*

Although algal growths, being restricted to the surface of beds, are not of primary importance in the direct purification processes, their luxuriant growths on the surface of some beds are probably of ecological importance and they may result in the choking of the bed. The following are the more commonly occurring forms considered ecologically important on bacteria beds:

Cyanophyceae *Phormidium*
Chlorophyceae *Ulothrix* sp.
*Stigeoclonium* sp.
*Monostroma.*

Associated with these are found unicellular types including diatoms, and, locally, mosses and liveworts may form luxuriant growths.

*Protozoa*

The protozoan fauna of bacteria beds is richer than that of activated sludge. This is probably due to the reduced interspecific competition because of the stratification possible in the beds. Such stratification has been demonstrated by several workers (Barker 1946), the species associated with a less-efficient activated sludge being found nearer the surface of the bed and those of a more efficient sludge, nearer the base of the bed, associated with the more purified state of the sewage. It was also found that the vertical distribution of these species at different works was affected by the strength of the sewage; seasonal changes, due to the sloughing of the film and possibly to temperature changes, also occur. Liebmann (1949) found horizontal as well as vertical zoning of microorganisms in bacteria beds. He also found that the vertical stratification was affected by the loading, the polysaprobic and mesosaprobic forms extending deeper into the bed the higher the load. The common species found in beds are probably the same as those listed for activated sludge. *Carchesium*, which is abundant nearer the bottom of the beds, is of more common occurrence.

## FACTORS DETERMINING THE
## ACCUMULATION OF FILM

The interrelationship and activity of these different members of the film are similar to those outlined for activated sludge, although modified to the extent that stratification is possible. By their combined activity the organic waste is removed or oxidized and as a result the microbial mass increases. Unless means were available for the removal of the excess film the beds would eventually choke.

In discussing the factors influencing film accumulation those affecting both the rate of growth of the film and its reduction must be considered. Within the bed, temperature, food and aeration are probably of primary importance in determining the rate of growth of the film. Increases in temperature up to 20° C result in increased rates of growth for most organisms of the film. Both the nature and strength of the sewage are important in considering the food supply of the film. The nature of the organic waste will determine the dominant organisms of the film.

As has already been mentioned different organisms increase their mass by different amounts whilst oxidizing the same amount of organic matter; zöogleal bacteria, for example, increase less than several common sewage fungi in breaking down a corresponding weight of glucose (*Water Pollution Research* 1955). The strength of the liquid fed to the bed affects the rate of growth of the film more than does the loading (strength and volume).

Being aerobic organisms, the rate of growth of organisms of the film will be restricted if the aeration of the bed is inadequate, as may occur when film accumulation has taken place or at times when the air currents through the bed are for other reasons reduced. Agencies operative in the removal of film have been described by different workers. British workers consider that the activity of the grazing fauna is of primary importance in the control of film, although Tomlinson (1942) has also reported the significance of bacterial attack on the hyphae of starving fungi. (Harrison, 1908; Johnson, 1914; Bell, 1926; Lloyd, 1945; Reynoldson, 1939; Tomlinson, 1946.)

American workers, on the other hand, consider that physical scouring by the liquid and microbiological activity of the film are most important, the activity of the macrofauna being considered incidental or at most having a minor role. (Lackey, 1925; Holtje, 1943; Heuke-lekian, 1945; Cooke and Hirsch. 1958.) Usinger and Kellen (1955), however, considered that the larvae of *Psychoda* were effective in film removal, thereby improving the efficiency of the bed.

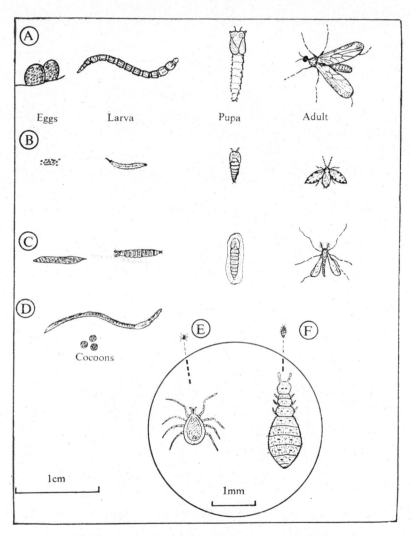

FIG. 3.2. Some macrofauna of bacteria beds; (A) *Anisopus fene-stralis*, (B) *Psychoda alternata*, (C) *Metriocnemus longitarsus*, (D) *Lum-dricillus lineatus*, (E) *Platyseius tenuipes*, (F) *Achorutes subviaticus*.

These different views may be explained to some extent by the more common use in America of high-rate filtration in which grazing fauna probably play a less important role than in the conventional filtration more common in the U.K. It is also possible that with the different films—bacterial, fungal and surface algal growths—and also at different degrees of film accumulation, the relative importance of the different contributory factors varies. Some of the causes suggested by American workers can only be opertative if the film is dominated by fungus (Holtje, 1943) and anaerobic decomposition of the film is more likely to be important only when considerable film accumulation has taken place. A further possible source of misunderstanding is that it has been assumed that the factor causing the seasonal unloading is necessarily the same as that which is reponsible for the continuous removal of film which takes place throughout the year. Observations at Minworth (Hawkes, 1957) showed that although the grazing activity of *Anisopus fenestralis* was important in controlling fungal film growths in the winter, the seasonal fluctuations in film were not accounted for by the differential effects of temperature on the grazing activity and on the film growth.

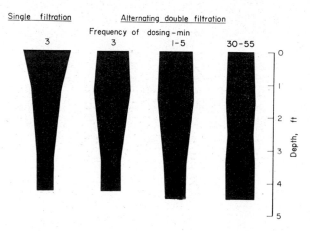

FIG. 3.3. Vertical distribution of film in bacteria beds operating under different conditions. (The two right-hand figures are drawn from data in TOMLINSON and HALL, 1955).

*The Vertical Distribution of Film*

The percentage distribution of film within a bed depends largely upon the volumetric loading and the instantaneous rate of application. Tomlinson (1946) found that the film was more evenly distributed in beds operated on alternating double filtration than in single-filtra-

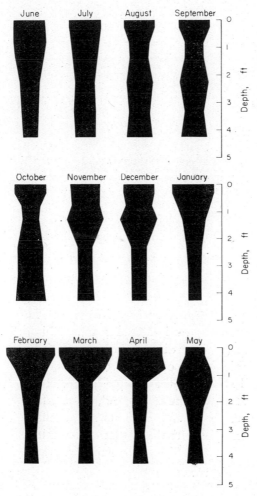

FIG. 3.4.   Seasonal fluctuations in the vertical distribution of film in a bacteria bed.

tion beds. Increasing the instantaneous rate of application by decreasing the frequency of dosing produced still greater evenness of distribution (Tomlinson and Hall, 1955). *Figure* 3.3 shows diagrammatically the percentage distribution of film in beds operating under different conditions; these represent average conditions for the year. As shown in *Fig.* 3.4 the vertical distribution may change seasonally in beds subject to film accumulation.

## GRAZING FAUNA

Ecologically the holozoic protozoa feeding on other microorganisms should be included in this group, but they are more usually considered as part of the film, as are the small metazoa such as nematode worms and rotifers. Their importance in controlling the film, however, should not be overlooked because they are less obvious. In experimental beds in which film accumulation was being studied in the absence of grazing fauna, discharge of humus solids was attributed to the large numbers of nematode worms which had accidentally become established. Of the larger members different species are dominant at different works, but the ones listed in *Table* 3.1 are probably the more widespread. Locally other species may dominate: the snail *Physa integra* and other snails are reported from some beds in America in such quantities that they were a serious nuisance by blocking pipelines, by abrasion of sludge-pump pistons and by becoming lodged in the mercury seals of distributors, thereby stopping them (Ingram *et al.* 1958). In this country *Lymnaea pereger* is common in the high-rate recirculation beds at Harrogate (Oliver, discussion Hawkes, 1957) and its presence there is attributable to the operating conditions.

Lloyd (1944) has shown that the grazing fauna of bacteria beds is derived from that of the mud-flats and, in a later paper (Crisp and Lloyd, 1954), these two environments are discussed to explain why so few of the members of the mud-flat community have been able to colonize the bacteria bed. Although toxic trade wastes limit the numbers of species, the chemical nature of sewage is not considered of primary importance in restricting the fauna. The physical environment and nature of the food are probably the most important factors limiting the macrofauna of bacteria beds. Of the sixteen species of *Psychoda*

Table 3.1. Macrofauna of Bacteria Beds

Oligochaeta (Worms)
  *Lumbricillus (Pachydrilus) lineatus*
  *Enchytraeus albidus*
  *Lumbricus rubellus*
  *Eisenia foetida*
  *Dendrobaena subrubicunda*

Insects
  Collembola (Spring-tails)
    *Achorutes subviaticus (Hypogastrura viatica)*
    *Tomocerus minor*
    *Folsomia* sp.
  Coleoptera
    *Cercyon ustulatus*
  Diptera (Two-winged flies)
    *Psychoda alternata*
    *Psychoda severini*
    *Psychoda cinerea*
    *Hydrobaenus (Spaniotoma) minima*
    *Hydrobaenus (Spaniotoma) perennis*
    *Metriocnemus hygropetricus (longitarsus)*
    *Metriocnemus hirticollis*
    *Anisopus fenestralis*
    *Paracollinella (Leptocera) fontinalis*
    *Scatella silacea*
    *Spaziphora hydromyzina*

Arachnida (Spiders and mites)
  *Lessertia dentichelis*
  *Porrhomma thorellii*
  *Erigone artica* var. *maritima*
  *Platyseius tenuipes*

in the Leeds district, all except one of which are so much alike that they require microscopical examination to identify them, only three are found in bacteria beds. Their liking for moisture and their ability to breed in confined spaces were considered important factors enabling them to colonize the beds (Lloyd, 1945). The unsuitability of the bed for pupation was also considered important in preventing its colonization by many insects. Although described as 'saprophytic' feeders, most grazers should be regarded as holozoic, feeding on the living ilm; they are rarely found amongst the truly saprozoic forms in sewage sludge (Hawkes, 1954).

7

The species which have been able to colonize the bacteria bed find the environment favourable for rapid multiplication. Seasonal temperature fluctuations are less marked in bacteria beds than in other more natural environments and insects which are capable of producing several generations a year do, in fact, produce more generations per year in bacteria beds than under natural conditions (Lloyd, 1945). Because of the natural selection by the environment there are fewer competing species for the available food, but at times when this is limiting severe interspecific and intraspecific competition takes place; under such conditions some—especially the chironomid flies—become predatory.

## FACTORS DETERMINING THE NATURE OF THE GRAZING-FAUNA POPULATION

Different beds support different grazing faunas and in determining the nature of the fauna several factors are probably involved. Beds treating normal domestic sewage usually have a full complement of grazing fauna, but a strong sewage tends to limit the fauna; *Psychoda alternata* and *Spaziphora hydromyzina* then become dominant. This may be due to the high oxygen-demand of the sewage or to the nature of the film it produces. Toxic trade wastes restrict the fauna to few species; different species probably react differently to specific toxic discharges, but generally *Psychoda alternata, Anisopus fenestralis, Achorutes subviaticus, Lumbricillus lineatus* and *Spaniotoma minima* are found in beds treating industrial sewages at Birmingham. At Huddersfield Reynoldson (1948) found the more resistant worm *Enchytraeus albidus* replaced *L. lineatus*. This further restriction in fauna to a few surviving species enables high populations to become established, with the consequent risk of fly nuisance. Just as physical factors were important in restricting the numbers of species colonizing beds, they are also most important in determining the nature of the fauna in different beds. The nature and size of the medium in the bed has been found to affect the relative composition of the fauna. At one works having beds of different-sized media it was found the larger medium favoured *Anisopus fenestralis* and the smaller medium *Psychoda alternata;* in the very fine medium ($\frac{1}{2}$ in.) of one bed *Lumbricus rubellus* was dominant. Terry (1951) attributed this to a thigmotaxic effect, whereby the organism tends to maintain the maximum contact between its body surface and the surrounding medium. Comparing four different media under identical operating conditions it was found (Hawkes and Jenkins, 1955) that in the bed having 2½ in. round-gravel medium *Lumbricillus lineatus* was the dominant grazer whereas fly larvae were dominant in smaller media.

It is possible that the form of the medium is also of importance: clinker or slag having many pits or depressions would provide a more hospitable niche than smooth gravel, for example. A further physical factor probably associated with the medium size is the downward rate of flow of the sewage over the stones; this obviously varies with the different methods of applying sewage to the beds, e.g. different rates of application and periodicity of dosing. At Minworth (Birmingham), beds receiving sewage as a gentle continuous spray supported a succession of dominant species including *Achorutes subviaticus, Psychoda alternata, Anisopus fenestralis and Lumbricillus lineatus*. Comparison with other beds treating the same sewage, but with increased rates of downward velocity from different operating conditions, showed that as the rate increased, *Achorutes subviaticus, Psychoda alternata* and *Anisopus* were successively eliminated leaving lumbricillid worms as the only effective grazing fauna in the alternating double filtration beds on which the distributors revolved once in 30 min, giving a high instantaneous dose and resultant high downward rate of flow. In beds served by distributors with spaced jets and no splash plates the downward flow varies horizontally across any one bed, being almost dry between the jet-lines in some beds. Although some lateral spread does occur as the sewage passes into the bed, this is not as great as had been thought when the bed is clean, and the upper zone of the bed, where the largest proportion of the grazing population are found, often provides two niches, one below the jet, where the downward flow may be great, and the other where there is hardly any flow. These conditions produce horizontal stratification of the fauna, lumbricillid worms and some fly larvae being found grazing on the film in the sub-jet zone, and *Achorutes* and other fly larvae (*Psychoda*) being more frequent in the interjet zone, which also provides suitable conditions for pupation of the larvae from the sub-jet zone. Because of the lack of flow humus tends to accumulate in the inter-jet zone and true saprobic types such as the beetle *Cercyon ustulatus* and *Spaziphora hydromyzina* occur here.

7*

The instantaneous rate of application also affects the vertical distribution of the macrofauna. High instantaneous rates limit some species such as *Psychoda* and *Anisopus* larvae and *Achorutes* in the surface layers, but after the initial flush is spent in the upper layers of the bed, the reduced scouring action permits fly larvae to become established within the bed. *Figure* 3.5(a) shows the relative distribution of *Anisopus* larvae in the upper 30 in. of different beds receiving sewage at different instantaneous rates because of different frequencies of dosing. Lumbricillid worms, being strongly prehensile because of their setae, are able to withstand considerable flushing action and their vertical distribution is less affected by the flow, *Fig.* 3.5(b); in fact the reduction in fly larvae by high instantaneous rates may result in an increased percentage of worms nearer the surface because of reduced interspecific competition (Hawkes, 1955).

Both the effect of medium size and downward rate of flow are affected by the degree of film accumulation. Even under the jets on large round medium where *Psychoda* larvae are unable to exist normally the development of thick fungal growths provides a suitable niche in which they become established. The amount of film accumulation may also determine the type of fauna: *Psychoda*, for example, is usually associated with thick film whilst *Spaniotoma* and *Metriocnemus* prefer a clean bed. It is also possible that the nature of the film, i.e. whether bacterial, algal or fungal, may have a selective effect on the fauna because of food preferences. Different operational practices may also affect the fauna. Lloyd (1945) attributed the absence of *Metriocnemus* in the Barnsley beds to the practice of resting for fortnightly intervals; because *Metriocnemus* is associated with the uppermost part of the bed and requires a constantly wetted surface it was thus adversely affected. The abundance of any species is largely determined by temperature, food supply and the abundance of competitors and predators. In beds treating domestic sewage, the number of competing species controls the abundance of any one species, but when the fauna is restricted by trade wastes, etc., reduced interspecific competition results in larger populations of the surviving species. Lloyd (1945) reported that the abundance of *Psychoda alternata* was successively greater in the beds at Leeds (Knostrop), Barnsley and Huddersfield, the fauna being successively poorer at the three localities. The seasonal incidence of any species is influenced by the number of other competing species present in the bed; the invasion of the bed by a new species may appreciably change the incidence of the species already present. Reynoldson (1948) found that the summer depletion of the fungal film at Huddersfield by *Psychoda* was the chief factor determining the incidence of the worm *Enchytraeus albidus*. The invasion of the Barston beds by *Anisopus fenestralis* was shown to have restricted the incidence of *Psy-*

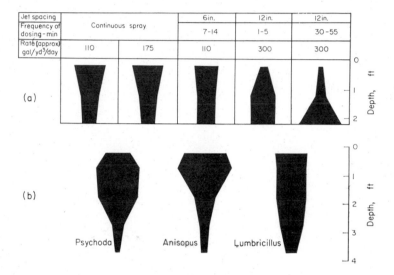

FIG. 3.5. (a) Distribution of *Anisopus* larvae in the upper $2\frac{1}{2}$ ft of bacteria beds to which sewage was applied at different instantaneous rates. (b) Comparative distribution of *Psychoda* larvae, *Anisopus* larvae and *Lumbricillus* worms in the same bed.

*choda* to August, September and October, whereas previously it was common between April and November (Hawkes and Jenkins, 1951).

At higher temperatures, up to the optimum, insects complete their life cycles more rapidly and, other things being equal, the population will tend to increase more rapidly. Because different species have different thermal requirements there is a succession of dominant species throughout the year in beds with a mixed fauna (Lloyd, 1945). Lloyd (1941, 1943) also showed that periods of maximum abundance of sewage flies are not brought about by a gradual increase in numbers, but by a series of alternating peaks and depressions, and the subsequent decline is in like manner; this type of incidence is induced by sudden changes in temperature.

In beds with restricted fauna the food supply in the form of the film is probably the most important limiting factor in controlling populations. At Minworth, where *Anisopus fenestralis* is the dominant grazer for most of the year, its relative seasonal abundance and incidence can be accounted for by the amount of film in the different beds (Hawkes, 1952). It was found experimentally that shortage of food not only resulted in a higher mortality of the larvae due to intraspecific competition, but the larval phase was lengthened and the resultant flies were smaller (Hawkes and Jenkins, 1951). Excessive film accumulation, although providing ample food, may create conditions unsuitable for the grazing fauna, the population of which is thereby suppressed. *Figure* 3.8 shows that when the fungal growths in a bed produced anaerobic conditions the fauna was seriously reduced.

The value of the grazing fauna in controlling film has already been discussed; it is possible, however, that they play a more direct role in the process. In small-scale experimental beds both Parkinson and Bell (1919) and Reynoldson (1939) reported increased nitrification following inoculation with *Achorutes* and *Lumbricillus lineatus* respectively. Dyson and Lloyd (1933) likened the grazing activity of *Achorutes* to the predatory activity of the holozoic ciliates whose activity maintained the bacteria in an active physiological state. Their grazing however would be expected to remove bacteria and protozoa indiscriminately as film and according to the "law of disturbed averages" by Volterra (see Macfadyen, 1957 p. 173) if two species are uniformly destroyed in proportion to their abundance, the mean numbers of prey increase and of predators decrease. On this basis the grazing activity of the macrofauna would tend to favour the bacterial population.

The introduction of *Lumbricillus lineatus* to similar experimental beds at Birmingham, which were, however, already clean by virtue of recirculation, produced no increase in nitrification, so it may well be that the increased nitrification reported by previous workers, reflected improved bed conditions. Because insects excrete nitrogen in the form of uric acid or ammonium compounds, readily capable of oxidation, their activity would be expected to assist in the biochemical breakdown of the film.

Unfortunately, although beneficial in the process of purification, the abundance of some members of the grazing fauna gives rise to considerable nuisance on and around sewage works. *Psychoda alternata, Anisopus fenestralis* and less frequently chironomid flies have been reported as causing a nuisance when numerous; although non-biting, because of their close association with sewage, their presence in the home must be considered a potential menace to health. *Culicoides nubeculosus*, a troublesome blood-sucking midge, is present on some works. An operator has not only to run his plant to achieve efficient purification, but must do so without causing nuisance in the vicinity; the prevention of fly nuisance is his duty.

## FACTORS INFLUENCING THE FILM-GRAZING FAUNA BALANCE

The factors affecting the nature and abundance of the two sections of the bacteria bed community have been discussed. The different populations, however, exist in a dynamic state of balance. The inter-relationship of these populations involved in the breakdown of organic matter in a bacteria bed is shown in *Fig.* 3.9. The effect of chemical, physical and biotic factors on this balance of populations will now be considered.

### Chemical Factors

The nature of the organic waste being treated largely determines the nature of the film. This may in turn affect the grazing fauna, which may also be affected directly by the waste especially if toxic. With some wastes, although they are amenable to biological oxidation in bacteria beds, the resultant film is not suitable food for grazing fauna, with a result that the beds eventually become choked. At Stoke-on-Trent, experimental beds, successfully treating gas liquor, broke down due to the coating of the medium with a dark-brown resinous matter, probably derived from the higher tar acids present in the liquor (Pickering, 1958). Apart from the collembolan *Folsomia* sp. a few of which were found near the base of the bed, the bed was devoid of grazers and tests carried out showed that the film was not taken by several common grazers. Because of the differential toxicity to the film and fauna, some wastes, although permitting film growth—usually fungal—suppress the grazing fauna with the result that the bed chokes. Less toxic substances restrict the fauna to a few species and the reduced interspecific competition may lead to fly nuisance. These chemical factors are imposed by the waste to be treated and apart from pretreatment and trade-effluent control in the case of sewage, the only practical method of varying it is by dilution by such means as recirculation.

Intentional additions of chemicals to the sewage are sometimes practised. When these are made to correct the waste either nutritionally in the case of some trade wastes, or to adjust the pH, they may be considered as modifications to the environment to encourage the suitable organisms for purification. The spasmodic application of chemicals, such as the liming and salting of beds to remove slime and the applications of insecticides in an attempt to alter the biological balance, although necessary palliative measures, are ecologically unsound. Hawkes (1952) showed that, by suppressing the *Anisopus fenestralis* population early in the year by insecticide treatment, the film remained available as food for later generations, which as a result were larger than in the untreated beds where the population was controlled by the limited food supply, the film having been removed by the earlier generation. Although successive applications of insecticide changed the fauna to one dominated by *Achorutes* this could only be maintained by expensive insecticide treatments and when these were suspended the normal fauna was rapidly re-established (Hawkes, 1955a).

*Physical Factors*

The size and nature of the medium used in a bed have probably more effect on the grazing fauna than on the film. With large medium excessive film accumulation can be better accommodated, with the result that the efficiency is less affected (Hawkes and Jenkins 1958). However, under clean conditions beds with smaller medium are more efficient. It should be the policy, however, to prevent excessive accumulation of film and not to design to accommodate it, and therefore small medium is the ideal.

The downward rate of flow of the waste through the bed can be varied at equivalent overall dosage rates by recirculation, double filtration, the frequency at which doses of the waste are applied to the bed, and the type of nozzle through which it is discharged. Although this factor affects both film and fauna, the effect on the film is largely restricted to the surface and below the surface the fauna is affected to a greater extent than the film. It has been claimed that film accumulation can be prevented by the flushing action of the sewage and the success of alternating double filtration and low-frequency dosing, i.e. heavy doses at infrequent intervals, has been attributed to this physical scouring because of the high instantaneous dosage rates. Although these forces may be operative in removing humus solids previously detached by other means such as grazing, fungal growths are able to withstand very great scouring action as is shown by their presence on the impeller blades of rotary pumps revolving at approximately 1000 r.p.m. Although immediately below the jet the fungal growths may be limited to *Fusarium* and *Geotrichum*, below the surface layer the downward flow of the liquid, although in some cases great enough to affect the grazing fauna, is not considered to have any significant effect on the film within the bed. Thus, because of the differential effect of the rate of downward flow, the film accumulation may be greater at higher instantaneous rates of dosing. Testing six types of distributor nozzle through which the sewage was discharged to the bed at different forces and differently distributed (*Fig.* 3.6) it was found that because of the suppression of the grazing fauna where the flow was great the film accumulation was greatest. Where horizontal stratification occurred due to jet spacing the two niches thus provided permitted *Anisopus* larvae and *Achorutes* to exist together. Where the distribution was even, these two grazers were in direct competition, *Achorutes* only becoming abundant when the *A. fenestralis* population was reduced in the summer. The continued grazing activity of the two populations is considered desirable and on this basis, jets spaced at intervals, were considered preferable to even distribution (Hawkes, 1959).

Temperature also has a complex differential effect on the film-fauna balance. The rate of increase and activity of both film and fauna is generally greater at higher temperatures within the range usually experienced in beds. Therefore the higher general metabolic activity within the bed results in enhanced purification at higher temperatures. Low temperatures suppress the grazing activity more severely than the growth of film and this differential effect has been claimed to account for the winter accumulation of film. With a purely bacterial film this is probably the case. *Figure* 3.7. shows the seasonal fluctuations of film and fauna in relation to temperature in beds treating domestic sewage and having a bacterial film. The increase in film coincided

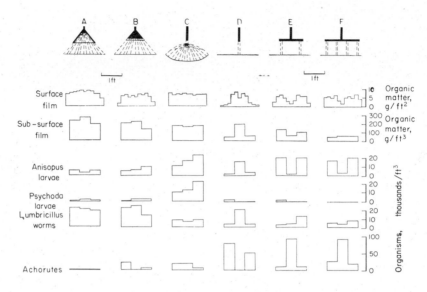

*Fig.* 3.6. Comparison of film and fauna in a bacteria bed under six types of nozzle arrangement on one distributor, each discharging equivalent volumes of sewage. (A) *Open fish-tail*, in which the jet from the $\frac{7}{8}$ in. diameter nozzle is discharged over a triangular tray slightly inclined from the vertical to produce a sheet of liquid *approximately* 24 in. wide at the surface of the bed. (B) *Closed fish-tail*, whereby the sewage is discharged through a rectangular orifice 9 in. long and $\frac{1}{4}$ in. wide to produce a sheet of liquid approximately 24 in. wide but with a somewhat stronger impinging force. (C) *Splash plate*—a circular disc $2\frac{1}{2}$ in. diameter on to which the jet was first allowed to impinge, producing a circular sheet of approximately 24 in. diameter. (D) The *unmodified nozzle* producing a cylindrical jet of liquid of approximately 1 in. diameter. (E) *Twin jets*—whereby the jet was divided into two by means of a horizontal pipe having two $\frac{3}{4}$ in. holes through which the sewage is discharged downwards onto the bed as two jets 12 in. apart, the total volume being equal to that discharged through one unmodified jet. (F) *Quad jets*—Similar to (E) but having four $\frac{1}{2}$ in. jets, each 6 in apart.

with a suppressed grazing fauna in the winter and the reduction in film with a rise in the grazing-fauna population—dominated by *Psychoda*—in the spring. With fungal growths, although growth is more rapid at summer bed temperatures, the rate of decomposition is also greater and thus the rate of accumulation is not necessarily increased.

*Figure* 3.8 shows the relationship between fungal film and grazing fauna; although successive generations of fly larvae modulated the film incidence, they were not the cause of it. Whatever the cause, however, the winter accumulation of film and reduced efficiency are associated

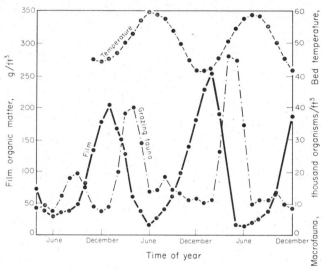

FIG. 3.7. Seasonal fluctuation of film and fauna in a bacteria bed treating domestic sewage.

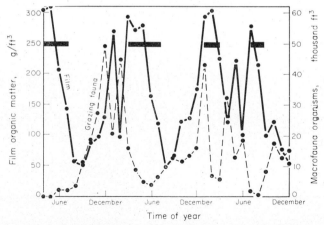

FIG. 3.8. Seasonal fluctuation of film (full line) and fauna (broken line) in a bacteria bed treating industrial sewage. (The black bars indicate periods when film was anaerobic).

with lower temperatures and in many cases these are a limiting factor in the winter operation of beds. Siting of the beds and the temperature of the waste both affect the bed temperature.

If the aeration of a bed is brought about by the differences in temperature throughout and above the bed, then because of the greater seasonal fluctuations in air temperature than in bed temperature, the aeration will vary throughout the year, usually being greater in winter than summer. This increased ventilation may result in increased fungal growths in the winter which then reduce the aeration (Petru, 1958).

*Biotic Factors*

The most important biotic factor affecting the balance of populations is the basic food supply entering the community, i.e. the waste. The strength of the waste determines the growth rate of the film which in turn determines the grazing fauna population. The growth rate can, however, be controlled by controlling the feeding as opposed to the food itself. Several practical methods of bed operation to control film are discussed in Chapter 6.

Although the film population and fauna population mutually affect each other, it is probably true to say that the amount of film is a more important factor determining the fauna population than the converse. In more natural environments, factors controlling animal populations are still not fully understood, but in bacteria beds the food supply is the most important factor (Hawkes, 1952). The soundest way to control a fly population breeding in the bacteria beds, therefore, is by controlling their food supply, i.e. limiting the accumulation of film.

The biological control of insects by the introduction of competitors or predators, operating as it does on a density-dependent factor, appears attractive for application in the enclosed environment of a bacteria bed. Although this method met with initial success in other fields, especially when applied to confined environments with an equable climate, such as tropical islands, it would appear that its applications are now becoming exhausted (Taylor, 1955). The fly *Spaziphora hydromyzina* is predatory on *Anisopus fenestralis* but, presumably because of its temperature requirements, it occurs later in the summer than the peak *Anisopus* population; it in turn is also highly parasitized by an ichneumon fly *Phygadeuon cylindraceus* (Baines and Finlayson, 1949).

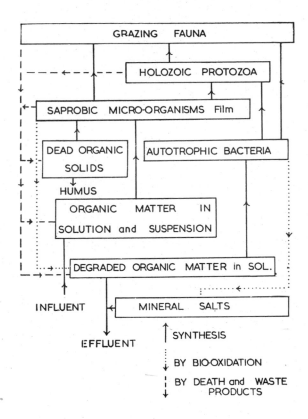

FIG. 3.9.   Diagrammatic representation of the main
paths of material transfer in the purification of organic
wastes in bacteria beds. [Reproduced from Hawkes
H.A. (1961)]. An ecological approach to some bacteria
bed problems, *J. Inst., Sewage Purif.*, (2) by kind permission of the editor.

CHAPTER 4

# THE APPLICATION OF ECOLOGICAL
# PRINCIPLES TO WASTE WATER
# TREATMENT — GENERAL

THE biological oxidation of an organic waste—sewage or industrial waste—either in bacteria beds or by activated sludge is basically the use of the organic matter as food by heterotrophic micro-organisms, mostly bacteria or fungi. Part of the waste is used as the fuel in respiration to produce the energy for life processes and is broken down to carbon dioxide, water and the usual end-products. A second portion, however, is synthesized into protoplasm in the form of new cells— the "film" of bacteria beds and the microbial flocs of activated sludge (*Fig.* 4.1). This microbial mass must be removed from the water before the effluent is discharged to the receiving stream. The subsequent

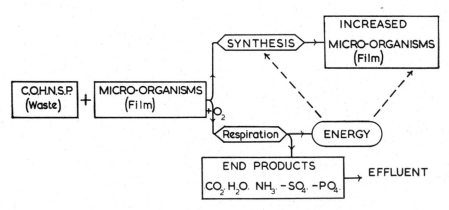

FIG. 4.1. Synthesis and energy production in biological oxidation of organic matter. [Reproduced from Hawkes. H.A., (1961)] An ecological approach to some bacteria bed problems, *J. Inst. Sewage Purif.* (2) by kind permission of the editor.

100

treatment and disposal of this sludge is outside the scope of our subject but the amount and nature of the sludge formed in the biological oxidation plant is of practical importance in this respect. American workers have reported that approximately half of the waste is resynthesized into microbial mass and half is respired (Sawyer, 1956). This proportion, however, varies with different wastes and, as previously mentioned, with different micro-organisms involved. In practice the amount of sludge produced will also vary with the method of operation depending on the degree of endogenous respiration involved.

## THE ROLE OF BIOLOGICAL OXIDATION IN WASTE WATER TREATMENT

Biological oxidation plants are best suited to treat organic wastes in solution or in non-settleable form. Inorganic compounds such as cyanides, sulphides, thiocyanates and thiosulphates, capable of being oxidized by autotrophic bacteria, may also be treated. The use of the adsorptive properties of the film or flocs to remove settleable matter, or matter not biologically oxidizable, should be strictly limited. Particulate matter is better removed by settlement, possibly preceded by a process of flocculation. Matter in solution which is incapable of biological oxidation, such as metallic salts, may prove injurious to the micro-organisms in the plant. Furthermore, although metals may initially be removed from the liquor by adsorption or even synthesized in the microbial growth, they cannot be broken down like organic matter. They may leave the plant as humus or as excess sludge, in which case they may cause difficulty in the treatment and subsequent disposal of the sludge. Another fraction, however, may return into solution as when the film in a bacteria bed is removed by grazing fauna or when film and activated sludge undergo auto-oxidation under conditions of starvation.

Stone (1955, 1956, 1958, 1959) found that with different metals different percentages (60—100) of the applied metal concentration appeared in the effluent. Of this amount different proportions were present in the humus and in solution; with copper, for example, approximately one third was in solution, whilst with nickel the amount was three quarters. Thus a considerable proportion of the applied concentration may appear in the final effluent after the settlement of the humus and result in a toxic effluent. The lethal concentration of the substances to stream life is probably much lower than that for microorganisms and grazers in the biological oxidation plants. Even though the concentration of metals in the waste does not seriously interfere with the biological oxidation, considerable reduction in toxicity may be needed to ensure a non-toxic effluent. It is possible that in treatment plants the metals become complexed with protein molecules, thereby reducing the toxicity. Metals may be present in wastes other than those from metal processing plants. Malt-distillery waste waters, for example, have been reported as containing $66 \cdot 0$ ppm Zn, $6 \cdot 0$ ppm Cu, $4 \cdot 5$ ppm Fe and $2 \cdot 0$ ppm Pb (Jackson, 1960). The metals were probably derived from the vessels and pipelines used in the process.

Radioactive wastes, like metals, cannot be destroyed in biological oxidation plants. Although radioactivity decays at a rate characteristic of the material, this rate, measured in terms of its half-life, cannot be altered by treatment methods. Belcher (1951) reported that certain radioactive substances were removed in biological oxidation plants; the radioactivity is transferred to the sludge, however, and the problem of disposal remains. The most widely used method for treating waste waters of low to medium levels of activity is by chemical precipitation, thus transferring the radioactivity to a solid phase, which of course still has to be disposed of (Burns, 1959).

In the latter half of the last century the association of such diseases as cholera and typhoid fevers with the polluted conditions of the rivers was probably a major factor in drawing attention to the need for adequate sewage treatment, even though the causative organisms were then unknown. The removal of pathogens is not now, however, generally considered a primary function of sewage treatment in this country. In America and in Russia much more attention is given to the bacterial standards of effluents. Although some plants effect a high degree of *Bact. coli* removal, some newer processes which are more efficient in the oxidation of organic matter are less efficient in reducing the number of *Bact. coli* (Allen *et al.* 1944). The B.O.D. of an effluent is no true indication of its bacterial content.

## THE ASSESSMENT OF PLANT EFFICIENCY

The purpose of waste water treatment is to prevent the pollution of the receiving water. Considering pollution as "an act which changes the natural qualities of the water in a river or stream" the ultimate assessment of the effectiveness of a plant is the extent to which the effluent affects the nature of the receiving water. What constitutes the "natural qualities" of water is the subject of some controversy because of the different interests involved. In this country, fishery interests in preserving the conditions of our streams suitable for fish life, to some extent safeguard the interests of others whose specific requirements may, however, differ. Aesthetic considerations, for example, should largely be satisfied. Public health requirements, however, are concerned both with the chemical content of the water and with the pathogenic organisms present. Although by satisfying the fishery requirements the chemical aspects are to a large degree safeguarded, the pathogenic content of the water is not usually considered important. Conversely a chlorinated water, satisfactory from a public health aspect, may be quite unsuitable for fisheries. In this country these two needs are satisfied by preserving the streams in as near natural condition as possible and chlorination is carried out after extraction for drinking purposes.

The discharge of an effluent may affect the natural quality of a water in several ways. These have been discussed at length elsewhere (Klein, 1957), (Hynes, 1960), and will only be briefly summarized here in discussing methods used to assess them.

*Organic Pollution*

Biologically oxidizable organic matter discharged to a stream is oxidized by micro-organisms as in the treatment plant. In the process the oxygen dissolved in the stream water is utilized and when the rate of removal is greater than the rate of re-aeration, resulting from surface aeration and the photosynthetic activity of plant life, the oxygen is depleted. Because of the time lag and flow of the stream, this deoxygenation is greatest some distance below the effluent and is followed by a recovery when the respiratory activity is successively reduced because of the progressive reduction in organic matter present. This phenomenon is known as the "oxygen sag" and the process as "self-purification". Synthesis, associated with the biological oxidation of the introduced organic matter, results in an increase in saprobic organisms—bacteria, fungi and protozoa—some of which form macroscopic growths attached to the stream bed; these growths are commonly known as "sewage fungus". Both the depletion of oxygen and the development of sewage fungus adversely affect the quality of the stream.

The potential oxygen demand of an effluent can be assessed directly by measuring the rate of oxygen uptake of a given volume of the effluent contained in a sealed vessel under carefully controlled conditions. Such manometric tests can be carried out over long periods and give not only the ultimate oxygen demand of an effluent but also a curve showing the course of oxidation. Techniques involving this principle, reviewed by Jenkins (1960), are unfortunately not practicable as routine tests for large numbers of samples. Manometric methods have, however, been suggested for B.O.D. determinations to eliminate errors due to dilution.

The biochemical oxygen demand (B.O.D.) has been generally accepted as a simple measure of the potential deoxygenating effect of the biologically oxidizable matter present in an effluent. It represents the oxygen uptake over the initial five-day period of the total respiratory curve. As a comparative test of the oxygen demand of effluents it is only strictly valid if the ratio of the B.O.D. to the ultimate oxygen demand is constant, i.e. if the respiratory curves are truly exponential. With sewage effluents it has been shown that their oxidation takes place in at least two definite stages representing the oxidation of carbonaceous and nitrogenous matter; sometimes two stages of nitrogenous oxidation are distinguishable—the first representing the oxidation of ammonia to nitrite and the second of nitrite to nitrate. These different stages result in definite steps in the oxidation curve (Fig. 4.2) and thus the ratio of B.O.D. to ultimate oxygen demand remaining will vary at different degrees of oxidation. From Fig. 4.2 it can be seen that it is possible for the B.O.D. over a five-day period to be greater when the oxidation is more advanced; compare, for example, the uptake between 5 and 10 days with that between 15 and 20 days when active nitrification was occurring. The implicit faith by some in the B.O.D. test is exemplified by the fallacious argument that nitrification is undesirable in sewage treatment plants because it tends to increase the

B.O.D. value! The same effect probably occurs with some effluents from plants treating mixed industrial organic wastes. Thus, although the B.O.D. is a simple and convenient test, care is needed in interpreting the results. Similarly, as pointed out by Wilson (1959), the efficiencies of treatment plants cannot be measured in terms of percentage B.O.D. removal unless the ratio of B.O.D. to the ultimate oxygen demand was the same for influent and effluent.

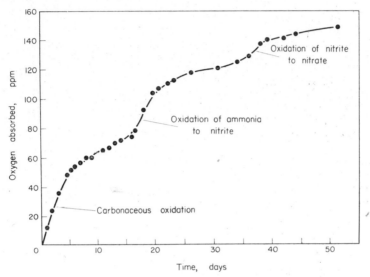

FIG. 4.2. Oxidation curve for a diluted settled sewage. (After Gameson, A.L.H. and Wheatland, A.B., *J. Inst. Sewage Purif.*, (2) by kind permission of authors and editor.

In contrast to these direct biological tests for assessing the oxygen demand, chemical tests are also used. By determining the oxidizable substances present in the effluent and knowing the course of oxidation, the theoretical ultimate oxygen demand can be calculated. Gameson and Wheatland (1958) calculated the ultimate oxygen demand for sewage effluents on this basis, accounting for the complete oxidation of the organic carbon, organic nitrogen, ammonia and nitrite by the equation

$$U.O.D. = 2 \cdot 67 \,(\text{organic carbon}) + 4 \cdot 57 \,(\text{ammoniacal N} + \text{organic N}) + 1 \cdot 14 \,(\text{nitrous N})$$

The results they obtained were in good agreement with those obtained by direct manometric methods. The above equation, however, assumes that the carbonaceous matter concerned has a respiratory quotient of unity, i.e. one volume of oxygen is utilized to produce one volume of carbon dioxide, one molecule of oxygen being required for each molecule of carbon. With sewage and sewage effluents this was apparently valid but other carbonaceous matter present in industrial wastes may have a different respiratory quotient and the figure of $2 \cdot 67$ C is not, therefore, necessarily generally applicable. Furthermore, although with the sewage effluents used, nearly all the organic matter was biologically oxidizable, with industrial wastes such as gas liquor, some may resist biological oxidation and therefore will not contribute to the oxygen demand, although it may represent a toxic fraction and therefore be of importance in assessing the overall polluting effect.

The determination of organic carbon is a lengthy process and for routine work the amount of oxygen absorbed from acid potassium permanganate or from boiling acid potassium dichromate is used as a measure of the oxygen demand. These two tests, the "Permanganate Value" (4 hr O.A.) and the "Dichromate Value" (Chemical Oxygen Demand) measure the chemically oxidizable matter present. These values do not represent the full oxygen requirements for the oxidation of all the biologically oxidizable organic matter. On the other hand they may include biologically stable organic matter.

The permanganate test is well established in sewage practice and pollution control in this country, probably because of its simplicity and the speed with which it can be carried out. It is, however, essentially an empirical measure and although of undoubted value in the operational control of individual plants continuously treating the same waste, its value as a comparative test is limited except for plants treating similar wastes such as domestic sewage. The relationship between the permanganate value, the B.O.D. and the ultimate oxygen demand varies considerably with wastes having different organic substances present. The dichromate value has been advocated in the *"Recommended Methods for the Analysis of Trade Effluents"* for industrial wastes because of its reproducibility and applicability to a wide variety of wastes. It has been suggested that it is more truly proportionate to the calculated ultimate oxygen demand than is the permanganate value.

For routine plant control one or more of these oxygen demand tests are necessary and where practicable these should be supplemented from time to time by determining the ultimate oxygen demand either by calculation or by manometric means.

However accurately the theoretical oxygen demand of an effluent can be estimated, the prediction of the actual deoxygenating effect of its discharge into a receiving stream is complicated by several factors. Dilution, rate of re-aeration, rate of oxidation, temperature and the biological condition of the stream are inter-related factors which must be taken into consideration. The extent to which the ultimate oxygen demand of an effluent needs to be satisfied by the stream depends on the time of retention of the oxidizable matter in the stream in relation to its rate of oxidation. The pertinent retention time is not necessarily that of the water, for flocculated solids may settle on the stream bed and soluble organic matter may enter food chains and be synthesized into living organisms, thus further complicating the oxygen balance. In lakes and estuaries with long retention times the full oxygen demand will probably have to be met. In certain circumstances, however, such as the pollution of a small tributary stream which at a short distance below the discharge, is greatly diluted on entering a major river, the rate of oxidation is probably more important in assessing the potential deoxygenation of the tributary stream itself. In such cases the B.O.D., which by involving a time factor (5 days), is to this extent a rate, is probably a more appropriate measure than the ultimate oxygen demand.

The actual deoxygenation resulting from a discharge can, of course, be measured by a series of dissolved oxygen determinations. Because of diurnal and seasonal fluctuations, large numbers of determinations are required, preferably a continuous record. A recording instrument for such determinations has been developed by the W.P.R. Laboratories (*Water Pollution Research*, 1956). Dissolved oxygen determinations, however, only measure one aspect of organic pollution—deoxygenation; the effects on the stream bed, where most of the stream organisms exist, are more difficult to measure analytically. Animal and plant communities living in the beds of streams exist in a dynamic state of balance which is very sensitive to changes in the environment. Organic pollution, by changing the environment, results in a change in the nature of the stream community to an extent depending upon the degree of pollution. Such effects have been studied by many workers and their results have been reviewed by Klein (1957) and Hynes (1960). Based on such findings the degree and extent of organic pollution can readily be assessed by the biological examination of the stream bed.

## Toxic and Physical Pollution

Some effluents affect the natural qualities of the water by addition of toxic or poisonous substances. Where specific substances are known to be involved these can be assessed analytically. In many cases, however, a whole range of substances may be present in the waste and then routine determinations could prove a formidable task. In such cases the biological assay of the toxicity of the effluent, using fish or invertebrate stream fauna as test animals, is sometimes practised. As with organic pollution, difficulties arise in using the results of such tests to predict the effects of discharges on streams. Even when full analysis is practicable, because of interactions involving synergistic and antagonistic effects and other factors such as pH and dissolved oxygen, it is difficult to predict the overall effect on a stream. Although bio-assay measures more directly the toxicity of an effluent to the animals used in the test, the effect on the complex stream community and environment in which organisms naturally exist is again difficult to forecast. In contrast to organic pollution, which by encouraging the activity of certain species causes a change in the balance of populations, toxic pollution tends to suppress activity generally. Because different species are tolerant of different concentrations of a given poison, it may result in a change in the relative balance of populations and in some cases the more tolerant species may increase in number due to the reduced interspecific competition. The general effect, however, is to reduce the numbers of individuals and the number of species present.

A discharge, although neither toxic nor deoxygenating, may affect the natural quality of the water by changing its physical properties. Discharges which appreciably raise the temperature, increase the turbidity or impart colouration are examples of physical pollution. Inert matter which settles on the stream bed may change appreciably the environment of the bottom dwelling organisms. Such deposits can seriously affect the spawning grounds of some fish, for example. Physical pollution usually has a marked effect on the stream organisms, especially when it affects the physical nature of the stream bed. In such cases it results in a change in the nature of the community; for example the deposition of solids on a naturally stony bed causes the replacement of a stone-loving fauna by one typical of silted conditions. Thus both toxic and physical pollution can readily be detected by biological examination of the receiving stream.

Apart from the above mentioned types of pollution the discharge of substances may alter the chemical nature of the water in other ways. Some readily oxidizable inorganic substances, such as sulphites in paper wastes, bring about simple de-oxygenation. Other wastes may alter the degree of hardness of the water or its salinity and thereby affect its natural qualities. Most effluents affect the receiving stream in more than one of the above mentioned ways. The type of tests chosen for operational control of a plant should be determined by the nature of the possible pollution and the nature of the receiving stream. In most cases such tests can with advantage be supplemented by biological examination of the receiving stream.

## THE CHOICE OF PROCESS-ACTIVATED SLUDGE OR BACTERIA BEDS

Many factors (and possibly some prejudices) will determine the choice of plant, but here we shall briefly consider the ecological considerations involved in a choice between the two most common biological oxidation processes used in this country—activated sludge and bacteria beds. The theoretical considerations have already been discussed. The sludges resulting from the two processes represent different energy levels, the activated sludge being of a higher energy order than humus sludge. Thus, from a point of view of energy conservation, activated sludge is superior. The "sludge" developed from certain wastes could possibly be exploited as animal feeding stuff; vitamin B.12 is extracted from activated sludge (Hoover *et al*. 1952) In sewage practice activated sludge is, however, more difficult to dispose of than humus sludge.

Activated sludge is generally more sensitive to fluctuations in flow and load and to toxic discharges than are bacteria beds. On the other hand, if a bacteria bed breaks down, due to overloading or toxic discharges, the period needed for the recovery of both micro-organisms and grazing fauna is longer than for the re-establishment of the simpler community of activated sludge. Some wastes, such as milk wastes, are not amenable to treatment by activated sludge because they tend to give rise to filamentous sludges which do not readily settle. Other wastes which are biologically oxidizable but which prevent the establishment of an efficient grazing fauna, or which cause solids to be deposited in the bed which are not readily removed, are best treated by activated sludge. Because of the longer period of maturation needed for bacteria beds, seasonal wastes and those which fluctuate appreciably in volume seasonally are best treated by activated sludge when possible. Since low temperatures have a less serious effect on activated sludge than on bacteria beds, the former are to be preferred for localities subject to severe winter conditions.

The more complex community of a bacteria bed, having organisms on several trophic levels, is more stable than that of activated sludge. Because of this, an activated sludge plant is more sensitive to chance changes in conditions, but for the same reason is more responsive to intentional changes imposed by operational control. Thus, with bacteria beds, less frequent adjustment to operating conditions is required. Activated sludge, however, is more amenable to frequent adjustments. The choice of plant will, therefore, be affected by the availability of experienced plant operators. The possibility of a greater degree of variability in bacteria bed operation, such as variable frequency dosing has, however, reduced this difference in the degree of plant control required. Other recognized comparisons between the two processes, such as operational costs, the inevitable linking of fly nuisance with bacteria beds, and the acceptance of non-nitrified effluents from activated sludge, all need to be re-assessed in light of developments in both processes.

## THE APPLICATION OF AUTECOLOGY IN DETERMINING A SUITABLE ENVIRONMENT FOR THE REQUISITE ORGANISMS IN BIOLOGICAL OXIDATION PLANTS

Although physical adsorption may account for the initial removal of organic matter from the waste water, the breakdown of the organic matter is the result of biological activity. The rate at which this occurs under optimum conditions depends on the readiness with which the micro-organisms are able to utilize the waste, this in turn is determined by the intrinsic properties of the waste and the respective micro-organisms. The theoretical rate at which a waste is oxidized biologically is known as the reaction constant (K) which is a measure of the oxidizability of the waste. In bacteria beds, according to Velz (1948) "the rate of extraction of organic matter per interval depth of a biological bed is proportional to the remaining concentration of organic matter measured in terms of its removability". Expressed mathematically —

$$\frac{L_D}{L} = 10^{-KD}$$

where  $L$   = Total removable B.O.D. in feed

$L_D$  = Remaining removable B.O.D. at depth D

$K$   = The reaction constant.

In practice, this maximum rate may be further limited by different environmental conditions imposed by the waste or by the plant. Such conditions may be studied in isolation in the laboratory but, as mentioned in our study of autecology, care must be taken in the application of the results. For example, the interaction of factors and their effect on the balance of populations must be considered. In this respect, results are probably more applicable to the simpler community of activated sludge than to bacteria beds. Nevertheless such studies provide results which, if intelligently applied, can give a useful guide as to the range of tolerance, if not indicating the optimum conditions for most efficient purification.

### Environmental Conditions imposed by the Waste

*Nutrition*—For those concerned with waste water treatment it is an encouraging thought that all naturally occurring organic substances and many synthetic ones are attacked by at least one species of microorganism and that organisms exist which are potentially capable of utilizing organic compounds not yet synthesized. The presence of specific substances in the waste, is therefore a most important factor in the environment. Some organisms are able to utilize a wide range of organic substances as their primary food source but others appear to be specific in their requirements. In the latter case it is necessary to ensure a continuous supply of the specific waste, or if this is not practicable, to retain a stock culture of the organisms.

All micro-organisms require certain basic nutrient elements—C, N, P, and S, together with certain trace elements such as K, Ca, Zn, Mg, Fe, Mn, Cu and Co. Furthermore the C, N, and P are required in roughly balanced amounts. In physiology the proportion of C to N is known as the C/N ratio; in waste water treatment practice it is usual to measure the C as B.O.D. and the proportion is then expressed as B.O.D:N or B.O.D : P. The optimum ratio for different organisms varies somewhat but as a basis for experiment a ratio of B.O.D : N : P of $100 : 6 : 1 \cdot 5$ could be used. The nitrogen is considered only fully available when present as $NH_3$ and the phosphorus as soluble $PO_4$, although other forms of nitrogen which can be converted into $NH_4$ may thus become available.

Domestic sewage usually provides a nutritionally balanced food with the necessary trace elements and vitamins for bacterial activity. The presence of a large proportion of trade wastes, however, may upset the balance. Some wastes such as those from milk processing and plastic manufacture may increase the carbon-nitrogen ratio and encourage troublesome filamentous growths. Pre-treatment of sewages containing trade wastes, before treatment in biological oxidation plants, may possibly upset the balance; a sewage with a high iron content, if subjected to a process of flocculation, could appreciably reduce the phosphate content for example.

Industrial wastes may be deficient in nitrogen, e.g. cider wastes, cotton-kiering wastes; or nitrogen and phosphorus, e.g. citrus waste, brewery waste and paper wastes (Helmers et al. 1952). Such deficiencies can be made good by the addition of the requisite amount of ammonium salt and phosphate to the influent. When practicable, domestic sewage could be used as a source of nitrogen and phosphorus although Wilson (1960) found that by supplying the phosphorus, deficient in a chemical manufacturing waste, by the addition of sewage, troublesome slime growths accumulated on the medium in the bacteria beds. As a result, agricultural grade triple super-phosphate was added to provide a concentration of phosphate in excess of that found necessary by laboratory tests—$0 \cdot 4$ ppm P. The actual amount of nitrogen and phosphorus required depends to some extent on the method of plant operation. In a plant where the organisms are subjected to endogenous respiration. the autolysis may release nitrogen and phosphorus for further synthesis—the carbon being lost as carbon dioxide. In treating wastes deficient in nutrients, the recycling of effluent containing a higher proportion of such nutrients may be one advantage of recirculation.

*Toxicity*—The presence of toxic substances in a waste may impair biological activity for reasons previously discussed. The structure of the bacteria bed film or sludge floc affords the embedded bacteria some protection against toxic flushes, but above certain concentrations they seriously affect the activity of the cells. In bacteria beds, toxic matter may be adsorbed on the film in the upper layers of the bed, thus reducing the concentration to which the film lower in the bed is subjected. No such protection is afforded in the activated sludge system where any part or all of the sludge may be subjected to high concentrations of toxic matter. This may be the reason why bacteria beds are usually considered better able to withstand toxic discharges.

It is not possible to state the concentrations at which different toxic substances seriously affect the efficiency of biological oxidation plants. For one thing, the toxicity depends upon such other factors as pH, dissolved oxygen, temperature and the presence of other toxic products. The toxicity of metallic ions in wastes admixed with sewage may be reduced if they are complexed with the proteins present in sewage. A further difficulty is the variation in sensitivity of the different organisms. Because of these complications, reference to the literatures gives a wide range of tolerable toxic concentrations. The heavy metals are usually considered toxic at above 1–3 ppm, but it has been reported by Ross and Sheppard (1956) that the efficiency of bacteria responsible for the oxidation of phenolic wastes from oil refineries was not affected by concentrations of copper up to 100 ppm. Under steady low concentrations of toxic substances it is possible that a more resistant micro-flora will become established, although this may not be as efficient as the original one. In this respect occasional strong toxic discharges are more serious than a steady weak discharge. As previously mentioned, however, metals are not amenable to biological oxidation and to ensure a non-toxic effluent their concentration in the feed should be reduced to a minimum.

Toxic non-metallic wastes such as phenols, thiosulphates, thiocyanates, cyanides, sulphides, formaldehydes, etc., although inhibiting the biological oxidation of other substances, are themselves subject to attack by specific organisms. Cyanides, for example, although interfering with biological treatment at concentrations between 1 and 2 ppm HCN (Lockett and Griffiths, 1947) (Pettet and Thomas, 1948), can be oxidized to ammonia and oxidized nitrogen in bacteria beds at concentrations of 60 ppm HCN without the addition of sewage (Pettet and Mills, 1954). Ware and Painter (1955) isolated an organism, an actinomycete, which proved capable of breaking down cyanides and which readily colonized bacteria beds. Where practicable such wastes are best treated separately. Since they are oxidizable to relatively non-toxic compounds they can be accepted in controlled concentrations for treatment at sewage works although this would necessitate a larger oxidation plant, both because of their slower rate of oxidation and their suppressing effect on the biological oxidation of the more readily oxidizable matter.

The partial oxidation of an industrial waste containing mixed compounds before discharging to the sewage works, although greatly reducing the oxygen demand and thereby reducing the load on the sewage works, may contribute a residual waste difficult to oxidize and possibly inhibitory to the biological oxidation of the sewage. Unless sufficiently diluted with sewage effluent it could also impart toxicity to the effluent. With wastes containing a mixture of such toxic compounds the oxidation of one may be inhibited by the presence of others. In the treatment of gas liquor, for example, the biological oxidation of the thiocyanate was found to be suppressed by the presence of phenols, and in practice did not occur until the phenol oxidation was almost complete (Pankhurst, 1959). Apart from the toxic effect of the phenol, interspecific competition between the heterotrophic phenol-oxidizing bacteria and the autotrophic thiocyanate-oxidizing organism may be involved, as is thought possible in the carbonaceous oxidation and nitrification of sewage. To overcome this inhibitory effect, gas liquor is being treated experimentally in a two stage process

—the first bed for the oxidation of phenols and the second for thio-cyanate oxidation (Pickering, 1958).

*pH*—Because enzymes are sensitive to pH changes it is not surprising that biological activity is affected by changes in pH. Different organisms have different pH optima and ranges of tolerance, acid conditions generally favouring fungi. Generally a pH between $6 \cdot 0$ and $8 \cdot 0$ is desirable for the biological oxidation of most wastes. Sewage is usually well buffered and its biological oxidation results in only a slight change in pH. With some industrial wastes, however, the change in pH as the waste is oxidized may be appreciable and create conditions unfavourable for further oxidation. The film or activated sludge floc may themselves act as a buffer against some degree of fluctuation in pH but are not able to withstand large changes. When a waste is oxidizable by different organisms, these may require different pH ranges. The bacterial oxidation of phenol is best effected between pH $6 \cdot 5$ and $7 \cdot 8$ but it is also successfully attacked by a fungus between pH $2 \cdot 0$ and $2 \cdot 5$ (Pankhurst, 1959).

## Environmental Conditions of the Plant

Biological oxidation plants are required to provide an environment in which the organisms and the waste are maintained in intimate contact in the presence of oxygen. In the activated sludge system this is ceffected by creating turbulent conditions in the aeration tanks by me-haical means, which at the same time introduces oxygen into the water from the atmosphere. In the bacteria bed similar requirements are satisfied by allowing the waste water to flow over a static film of micro-organisms, the oxygen being supplied by absorption from the air passing through the bed. Factors influencing the degree to which these conditions are provided will be discussed in the respective sections on activated sludge and bacteria beds.

The waste itself, of course, creates environmental conditions within the plant other than those already mentioned. Very strong organic wastes such as cotton-kiering liquor, food processing waste waters and distillery wastes, having a high oxygen demand, result in conditions of oxygen depletion in the immediate environment of the organisms. No matter how efficient is the aeration within the plant, the rate of oxygen uptake would exceed the rate at which it could be transferred from the air through the liquid to the organism. Such liquors should, therefore, be diluted with returned effluent or by other means to produce a liquor having a B.O.D not exceeding 350 ppm, to ensure the prevention of anaerobic conditions within the plant. Wastes having a very high oxygen demand, a B.O.D exceeding 1,000 ppm, are probably best pre-treated by anaerobic processes followed by the biological oxidation of the resultant weaker liquor. It has been found that to induce satisfactory digestion of soluble organic wastes it is necessary to introduce a solid matrix. Pettet and others (1959) reported that this can be satisfactorily achieved by adding a massive inoculum of actively digesting sewage sludge which, by gradually increasing the rate at which the waste is added, can be developed into an active anaerobic sludge.

This is retained in the system by settling the effluent from the digester and returning the settled sludge as in the aerobic activated sludge process. In other countries such anaerobic processes have been successfully applied to a variety of strong wastes including those from yeast production and fermentation processes (Underkofler and Hickey, 1954), meat packing (Steffen, 1958), and chewing-gum manufacture (Orford, 1951) in America, and yeast wastes in Denmark and Sweden (Southgate, 1948). Of the wastes investigated in pilot plants by the W.P.R. Laboratories in England, slaughterhouse wastes would appear to be the most amenable to treatment by anaerobic processes (Pettet *et al.* 1959), Meat wastes have also been successfully treated anaerobically in pilot plants in New Zealand by Hicks (1954).

Temperature is an important factor determining the rate of biological activity. Each species has a temperature range over which life is possible. Within this range activity increases with increase in temperature to an optimum above which the thermal denaturing of the enzymes occurs at a rapidly increasing rate, resulting in decreased activity and ultimate death of vegetative cells. Some micro-organisms, however, produce highly resistant spores capable of surviving temperatures outside the range of tolerance for the vegetative cell. Organisms active in aerobic treatment plants are usually mesophilic, having optima between 20°C and 40°C, depending on the species. Within the physiological temperature range, biological activity generally changes by a factor of 2 for each 10°C change in temperature. Manometric studies have shown that this factor, known as the $Q_{10}$ value, for activated

sludge was between 2·0 and 2·06, between temperatures of 0 and 25°C
(Wuhrmann, 1956).

In view of this significant effect of temperature on biological activity
it may be expected that plant efficiency would be similarly affected.
In fact, changes in temperature over a wide range of temperatures
have little direct effect on the efficiency of treatment plants. There is,
for example, little seasonal fluctuation in efficiency of activated sludge
plants with changes in temperature, although increased temperatures
could be expected to increase the efficiency both by increasing the

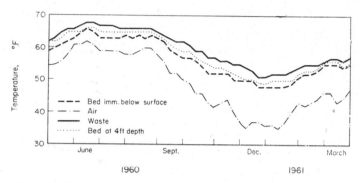

FIG. 4.3. Seasonal temperature fluctuations near the surface and
within a bacteria bed in relation to air and waste temperatures.

oxygen transfer rate as well as directly increasing biological activity.
Viehl and Meissner (1934) considered that the sludge organisms were
able to adapt themselves to counteract the effect of low temperatures.
Certainly, active sludges can be developed over a wide range of temperatures. Gehm (1956) investigated the treatment of waste waters
from the pulp and paper industry which had temperatures of between
50 and 53°C; he found that such wastes could be satisfactorily treated at
feed temperatures of 52°C by the activated sludge process, the efficiency being much the same as that between 30 and 40°C. Although sludges
can be developed to operate at different temperatures their efficiency
is reduced if they are subjected to violent changes in temperature.
In sewage plants such violent changes in temperature do not occur;
in plants treating specific industrial wastes, however, they could occur
due to sudden discharge of a hot waste. Although the temperature

near the surface of a bacteria bed is related to the temperature of the waste and the air temperature, the temperature within the bed is more closely related to that of the waste (*Fig.* 4.3). The temperature of the

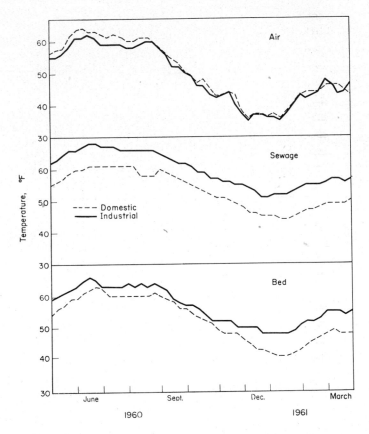

FIG. 4.4. Comparison of seasonal temperature fluctuations in a bacteria bed treating domestic sewage with one treating industrial sewage together with corresponding air and waste temperatures.

waste is, therefore, an important factor influencing the temperature of bacteria beds. Sewages containing industrial wastes are generally warmer during the winter than purely domestic sewages and thus beds treating sewages containing such wastes are not subjected to as low temperatures as are beds treating domestic sewage (*Fig.* 4.4). The effect of the waste on the bed temperature depends to some extent on the volumetric loading as well as its temperature. The higher volumetric loadings common with filtration methods used for industrial sewages would, therefore, tend to further enhance this temperature difference.

In bacteria beds marked seasonal fluctuations in efficiency may occur, but these are due to the indirect effect of temperature on the film-fauna balance, as discussed later. In experimental laboratory beds operated at different temperatures over a range 5°C–30°C, although large differences in temperature at different depths within each bed made strict comparisons difficult, it was apparent that there was little difference in the efficiency between 10°C and 30°C; at 7°C, however, there was a marked decrease in efficiency. Grazing fauna were not introduced into the beds and it was found that in the beds of similar efficiency—those operating berween 10°C and 30°C—the amount of accumulated film was the same, whereas in the beds operating at 7°C, less film had been accumulated. Thus this direct effect of temperature was only evident below 10°C. Ware (1958) found that the biological breakdown of cyanide in laboratory experimental beds was little affected by temperature changes in the range 10°–35°C, but that at temperatures outside this range, performance deteriorated rapidly. There was, however, a possibility that an organism other than the actinomyces, with which the bed had been inoculated, was active at the higher temperatures when recognizable actinomycetes were virtually absent.

The lack of the expected relationship between temperature and plant efficiency may to some extent be due to adaptation or changes in the microbial flora with changing temperature, but the absence of response to short term temperature changes is more likely to be explained in terms of limiting factors. The original theory, whereby it was considered that of the many factors influencing a biological process, only one was operative at any time and that this being so, the rate of the process could not be affected by changing the other, non-limiting, factors, is not now fully accepted. Nevertheless, by changing a factor which is not at the time limiting, the resultant effect on the process is only a fraction of that expected theoretically. On the other hand changing

9

a limiting factor causes the expected change in the rate of the process until such times as another factor becomes limiting.

In biological oxidation plants the ultimate factor limiting the rate of oxidation is the intrinsic rate of generation, under optimum conditions, of the micro-organisms concerned. Of the many factors theoretically capable of influencing this rate, the ones most commonly limiting, under normal operating conditions, are probably the rates at which food or oxygen are transferred from the liquid to the cells. With weak wastes such as domestic sewage the transfer rate of the respiratory substrate—the waste—is probably limiting but with strong industrial wastes it is probably the oxygen transfer rate that is limiting, at least in the early stages of oxidation. With the exception of the surface layers of some exposed bacteria beds in winter, temperature is generally not a directly limiting factor and rises in temperature do not, therefore, bring about the increase in rate of oxidation which would be expected from the experimental $Q_{10}$ value. Temperature, however, affects the transfer rates, but according to Wilson (1960a), with oxygen or nutrient availability controlling, a 10°C rise in temperature would increase the transfer rate and, thereby, the rate of biological oxidation, by no more than 20–30 per cent. He suggested that the response of a plant to temperature changes provides a rough indication of the operative limiting factors, the greater the temperature effect the less the control by oxygen and nutrient availability. As an example he quotes data from the Monsanto plant at Ruabon showing that the $Q_{10}$ value for a bacteria bed was 1·4 when the B.O.D. of the feed was 322 but was only 1·08 when the feed B.O.D. was halved.

A knowledge of which factor is limiting in any plant is, of course, important in plant operation. The principle of limiting factors may also explain the discrepancies in operational experiences which result in the advocacy of different and sometimes conflicting practices in treatment methods. The change in a factor, which in one plant produced marked improvements in efficiency, may give disappointing results in an apparently similar plant but where another factor is limiting.

## THE APPLICATION OF SYNECOLOGY IN CONTROLLING POPULATIONS AND THEIR ACTIVITIES IN BIOLOGICAL OXIDATION PLANTS

Although autecology enables us to define the conditions of a plant necessary for efficient oxidation, the operation of a plant involves the controlled activity of different populations and the transfer of materials and energy between the waste and the different populations; as such it involves us in synecology.

Of the several populations present in plants, the saprobic micro-organisms, including the autotrophic bacteria, are the organisms primarily concerned with the breakdown of organic wastes and it is, therefore, the control of their activity that is of primary importance. At first sight it would appear that maximum efficiency would be achieved by maintaining the organisms in a constant state of maximum growth, i.e. in the log phase (*Fig.* 1.12). In the absence of controlling factors, however, this phase cannot be indefinitely maintained. Of the several theoretical factors terminating the log phase, the impedence to the transfer of oxygen and nutrients to the increasing number of cells in the microbial mass—the activated sludge floc or the bacteria bed film—is probably the most important in biological oxidation plants. The accumulation of toxic metabolic by-products may also be a contributory factor.

For efficient operation, the organisms must remain physiologically capable of log growth and, therefore, the control of the microbial population is essential. Organisms in this physiological state may, however, be prevented from achieving maximum log growth by such factors as temperature, pH, dissolved oxygen and nutrient concentration. For maximum efficiency, of these factors, nutrient concentration should be the limiting factor, this, of course, being determined by the waste being treated. In practice, providing that the autecological conditions, previously discussed, are satisfied, the synecological considerations involve the establishment and maintainence of a balance between the loading imposed by the waste, the microbial population and the oxygen concentration. The optimum level at which this balance should be established and the operational methods by which it can be maintained in activated sludge plants and in bacteria beds will be dealt with in the next two chapters.

# CHAPTER 5

# ECOLOGICAL CONSIDERATIONS IN THE DESIGN AND OPERATION OF ACTIVATED SLUDGE PLANTS

THE intimate contact of the waste with an optimum quantity of active sludge organisms in the presence of adequate oxygen supply for a requisite period of time followed by the efficient separation of the organisms and purified liquor, are pre-requisites of the process.

The time of contact for a given flow is predetermined by the capacity of the aeration tanks which should be related to the strength, volume and treatability of the waste. The design, however, should provide for variability in the degree of aeration and in the amount of sludge carried in the system. Factors determining the optimum levels of these two variables in relation to the loading will now be discussed in the light of the reported results of several laboratory investigations and the operational experiences of several workers—mostly in America.

*Aeration.*—Before atmospheric oxygen becomes available to partake in the biological oxidation of the waste, it must be transferred to the seat of the activity—the respiratory enzymes within the cell of the organism. Four stages must be considered in this transfer:

(i) The transfer of atmospheric oxygen into solution in the waste water.

(ii) The transfer of the oxygen dissolved in the waste water to the surface of the respiring cell.

(iii) The diffusion through the cell wall and cell membranes into the cell itself.

(iv) Finally, the absorption by the appropriate respiratory enzyme.

The last two steps in the transfer are governed by the properties of the cells themselves, although they may be affected by the nature of the surrounding waste water. Work by Winzler (1941) supports the view that the limiting factor at low dissolved oxygen concentrations was the rate at which oxygen was absorbed by the enzymes and not the rate of diffusion of oxygen into the cell. In practice, however, it is necessary to maintain the dissolved oxygen concentration at the surface of the cell at a sufficiently high level to ensure the saturation of the oxygen-bearing enzymes. In plant operation this concerns us with the first two stages of oxygen transfer. Of these, the initial transfer rate of the atmospheric oxygen into solution, in the different methods of aeration, has received much attention (McCabe and Eckenfelder, 1956). The dissolved oxygen concentration at the surface of the cells in the floc may, however, be quite different from that in the body of the water. To ensure adequate transfer to the cells in the floc it is necessary to ensure the movement of floc relative to waste water by creating turbulent conditions within the tank, as opposed to the general circulation of the liquid in which the flocs could be carried in the same pocket of liquid. Pasveer (1956) calculated that the oxygen concentration at the boundary of the floc in the case of slight turbulence was only a small percentage of that existing in the case of strong turbulence. Gaden, (1956) applying the results of work on the effects of agitation and aeration in fermentation processes, stresses the importance of agitation in the activated sludge process. He considered that air bubbles had distinct limitations as agitators. Ciliate protozoa probably assist in the aeration of the floc by producing micro-currents (Lloyd, 1945).

The oxygen concentration at the surface of the individual cells within the floc will also depend upon the size and texture of the floc itself. Wuhrmann (1960) has calculated that in a liquor having a dissolved oxygen concentration of $1 \cdot 5$–$2 \cdot 5$ ppm the flocs should not exceed 400–500 $\mu$ in diameter, if the innermost cells are to receive an adequate supply of oxygen. The structure of the floc is also probably of importance in this respect; microscopic examination of sludges reveals that some flocs have a dense appearance, whilst others are of a more open structure. Filamentous growths, although affecting the settling qualities of the sludge, present a loose, open floc with high oxidative powers.

Most micro-organisms in biological oxidation plants are micro-aerophilic, i.e. require only a low dissolved oxygen concentrations (less than 1 ppm.) for optimum activity. Many workers have reported that the respiratory rate of activated sludge is independent of the dissolved oxygen concentration above about 1–2 ppm., providing that turbulence is adequate (Dawson and Jenkins, 1949) (Wuhrmann, 1956) (Okun and Lynn 1956).

The rate of aeration should supply oxygen to balance the uptake by the floc in order to maintain the necessary concentration throughout the aeration tank. This demand will depend upon the rate of uptake of substrate (the waste) by the floc, this rate largely being determined by the concentration of the waste. Domestic sewage is a relatively weak nutrient solution and normally the rate of oxygen uptake will exceed the uptake of the nutrient and is not, therefore, limiting. With strong industrial wastes, however, the nutrient uptake may exceed that of oxygen which would then be limiting. The degree of aeration should, therefore, be related to the B.O.D. loading of the plant rather than to the volumetric loading. The greatest oxygen demand occurs at the inlet end of the aeration tank, where the waste and the de-oxygenated sludge enter. As purification proceeds and the oxygen demand is reduced, lower rates of aeration are possible. In such modified methods as "tapered" aeration, the degree of aeration is highest at the inlet end of the tank and is reduced with declining oxygen demand along the tank. The initial high oxygen demand is also prevented in methods in which complete mixing is practised, and to some extent in step aeration, where the waste is introduced into the aeration tank at different distances along the tank.

It would appear that when oxygen is the limiting factor it is often the second stage—the transfer of oxygen dissolved in the waste to the surface of the cells—that is limiting, due to insufficient agitation. Increased purification rates claimed for different methods of aeration, such as brush aeration and coarse bubble aeration, may be due to the increased agitation, rather than to the introduction of larger amounts of oxygen. Several workers have, however, reported increased rates of purification by increasing the rates of aeration (Pasveer, 1959) (McNicholas and Tench, 1959) (Wuhrmann, 1960). The two latter workers considered that this enhanced purification was due to a change in the species composition of the sludge, which became biologically adapted to the higher dissolved oxygen concentration. The more aerobic organisms which replace the micro-aerophilic species presumably have a higher rate of metabolism. Both workers reported changes in the microscopical appearance of the sludges. The process of aeration, besides providing the necessary oxygen and turbulence necessary to ensure the intimate contact of waste, oxygen and organisms, may also assist in the scrubbing out of the toxic end products of metabolism, which would otherwise accumulate in the floc.

Most workers agree that the period of deoxygenation resulting from conditions in the settlement tanks may have a deleterious effect on the sludge and should, therefore, be reduced to a minimum. The establishment of a high dissolved oxygen concentration in the effluent from the aeration tanks may reduce the extent of deoxygenation in the settlement tanks, but this is probably better achieved by ensuring that the sludge load is well oxidized and therefore exerts only a small oxygen demand in the settlement tanks. Wuhrmann (1956) found, as a result of manometric tests, that the rate of disappearance of a soluble substrate was paralleled by its oxidation in respiration, contrary to the general concept of initial adsorption and storage. Later work (Wuhrmann, 1960) showed that washed activated sludge, after periods of anaerobiosis for 1–4 hours, showed no difference in respiratory rates when aerobic conditions were again established. He concluded that the periodic anaerobiosis in the activated sludge cycle was probably less detrimental than is generally assumed. With soluble substances, which are oxidized as they are removed from the waste water, this may be so. However, with wastes such as sewage, in which much of the load is in the form of suspended or colloidal solids which are first adsorbed and subsequently oxidized, the presence of unoxidized adsorbed solids in the floc under conditions of anaerobiosis and quiescence in the settlement tanks, could be detrimental to the condition of the sludge. Under such quiescent conditions there could be little or no removal of the toxic end products of anaerobic decomposition from the floc, the accumulation of which could impair the efficiency of the sludge.

Until further evidence is produced on a wider range of wastes it would seem wise to accept the view that prolonged deoxygenation of the sludge is detrimental and to provide for the rapid return of the sludge to the aeration tanks. This involves the provision of adequate pipe-work and pumping capacity; the rate of return will then be determined by the rate of settlement of the sludge in the settling tanks. This factor is determined by the characteristics of the sludge itself, which will be discussed in the next section. By using two-stage settlement it should be possible to settle out most of the sludge in the first tank with relatively low retention time; to provide for the sludge return, and to complete the settlement of the remaining sludge in large secondary tanks, the settled sludge from which could be passed to waste.

*Sludge characteristics*—The ecological unit of the sludge is the floc and it is the structure and biological condition of the individual flocs that determine the general efficiency of the sludge. To be efficient the floc must satisfy two quite distinct conditions; it must first remove the waste from the water and secondly it must itself be capable of being readily separated from the purified liquor by settlement. These two characteristics are not necessarily linked; a young actively growing floc, capable of rapid removal of waste, may have poor settling properties; on the other hand a good settling sludge may have reduced powers of oxidation.

Different theories have been put forward to explain the mechanism of the removal of organic matter from waste waters by activated sludge. Whilst it is not the purpose of the present work to discuss such theories, it is necessary to formulate a theory as a working hypothesis for the correlation of experimental evidence and operational experience. One must, however, be willing to change or modify a theory to accommodate any new and valid evidence or experience, one's sense of judgement being consoled by the thought that in science there is no such thing as the ultimate truth!

The floc may be considered as being formed initially as the result of combined biological activity and physical forces when waste water containing the necessary inoculum of micro-organisms is aerated. The types of micro-organisms which develop depend upon the nature of the waste as previously described. Bacteria rapidly multiply and at first are freely dispersed in the liquid but later agglutinate to form the primordium of the floc. McKinney (1956) considered that the flocculation of bacteria occurred only when their energy level was reduced sufficiently to prevent them from overcoming the physical forces, such as the Van der Waals forces of attraction, causing them to adhere. Thus flocculation was more likely to occur in reduced nutrient concentrations. He considered that this power of flocculation was common to all bacteria and was not confined to a few zöoglea forming species. Nevertheless this tendency to flocculate probably varies with different species and the difficulty experienced in developing a floc in some plants treating specific trade wastes, may be due to the dominance of a species peculiar to the waste. Such difficulties have been experienced in the treatment of phenolic wastes (Broughall *et al.* 1960); although aeration resulted in a marked reduction in the phenolic content, the dispersed bacteria imparted turbidity and a high B.O.D. to the effluent. The difficulty was overcome by discharging the effluent together with the suspended bacteria into lagoons where clarification took place, presumably due to flocculation of the bacteria under conditions of low nutrient concentrations.

Renn (1956) stressed the importance of physical forces associated with interfaces—both air–water and solid–water—where, in the case of organic matter in low concentrations as in waste water, the organic matter tends to be concentrated. These forces, he suggests, are operative on the dispersed bacteria themselves and result in the interfacial trapping of the bacteria at the air-liquid surface of the bubbles and their consequent flocculation. The bacteria in the resultant floc become embedded in a common gelatinous matrix which forms a further solid-liquid interface at which the organic waste is then concentrated. This waste is then used by the bacteria for respiration and synthesis, the resultant multiplication increasing the size of the floc. The relative rates at which the waste is removed and oxidized by the floc is still a matter of controversy. Many workers (Ridenour, 1935) (Haseltine, 1956) (Katz and Rohlich, 1956) consider that the organic matter is first rapidly adsorbed by the floc and that the accumulated waste is subsequently oxidized as aeration continues. This view is supported by the observation that the initial rate or removal of organic matter was many times greater than could be accounted for by the respiratory rates (Gellman and Heukelekian, 1953). It was considered that the rate of removal of soluble organic matter such as glucose was according to the simple adsorption equation (Ruchhoft *et al.*, 1940). In later work, however (Ruchhoft *et al.*, 1940a), it was found that no glucose could be removed from sludge which had previously removed considerable quantities of it. It was assumed that it had been absorbed by the floc. Wuhrmann (1956) found that the substrate respiration of the sludge ceased immediately the glucose substrate was exhausted and concluded, therefore, that no glucose had been adsorbed on the floc surface. Porges *et al.* (1956) found that the rate of purification of dairy wastes was twelve times the rate of oxidation. As a result of chromatographic analysis they concluded that some of the carbohydrate waste was stored in the cells as an insoluble glycogen-like substance which was subsequently oxidized.

It would appear that adsorption and absorption both result in the initial removal of waste. With wastes having suspended and colloidal organic matter, their adsorption on the floc surface accounts for the initial rapid removal of waste. Some of the adsorbed matter is then readily absorbed, while other more complex molecules are broken down by the action of enzymes secreted by the cell, before being absorbed. A further fraction may be incapable of being absorbed and remains in the floc as relatively inert matter. In some industrial wastes most of the organic matter is in solution; in such cases it is possible that the waste is absorbed immediately it has been adsorbed, in which case no accumulation of the waste takes place on the floc surface. The relative rates of absorption and oxidation of the waste will probably depend upon the concentration of the waste; with a strong waste, organic matter may be stored and be available for subsequent oxidation, with a weak waste or one which is diluted as in the complete mixing systems, oxidation may proceed simultaneously with the absorption of the waste. The extent to which the waste is accumulated either on the surface of the floc or as storage products within the cell, depends upon the relative rates of adsorption, absorption and oxidation in relation to the concentration of the waste.

The floc may thus increase in size by multiplication of the bacteria within the floc, and by the addition of living and non-living matter from the liquid. During development, the floc becomes colonized by bacteria-feeding organisms such as ciliate protozoa, nematode worms and rotifers. Thus a mature floc can be regarded as a microcosm, the populations of which exist in a dynamic state of balance sensitive to the environmental changes including the waste itself. Some ciliate protozoa such as *Paramoecium*, *Colpidium* and *Lionotus* swim freely in the interstitial liquid and cannot be considered as associated with the floc. Others, mostly belonging to the Hypotricha, such as *Aspidisca* and *Euplotes*, have cilia modified as cirri for creeping over surfaces and are distinctly associated with the floc as, of course, are the attached ciliates *Vorticella*,

*Opercularia* and *Epistylis* which are anchored to the floc by their stalks. Microscopical examination suggests that the free swimming forms prey on the bacteria dispersed in the liquid, whereas the creeping forms, which can be seen browsing amongst the flocs, are actively controlling the bacterial population of the floc as do the nematode worms and rotifers. The attached ciliates, however, although closely associated with the floc physically, appear to feed upon the dispersed bacteria. They can be seen to bring about the flocculation of bacteria and other dispersed solids by ingestion and the subsequent ejection of larger particles as demonstrated by Sugden and Lloyd (1950).

As the floc grows and ages, a higher proportion of it consists of dead cells and accumulated inert solids. Although the former may still be capable of enzymatic secretion (Wooldridge and Standfast, 1933) and the whole floc capable of adsorption, oxidation is only possible by the active living cells and thus there is a decline in the general activity of the floc as it ages. Also as the floc increases in size, the diffusion of nutrients and oxygen to the individual cells, and that of waste products out of the floc, becomes more difficult. Thus, as with cultures, each floc may be considered as passing through different phases of growth, reaching maturity and then declining. The pressure of predatory populations delays the decline phase of the floc. In passing through these phases the floc changes in structure and in activity, both important features in operation. Several workers (Keefer and Meisel, 1953) (Wuhrmann, 1956) have reported the gradual reduction in substrate removal rate with increasing sludge age.

The acceptance of this concept is implicit in the American use of "sludge age" in the operation of activated sludge plants. This may be defined as the average total time of detention of the flocs in the system. At a constant sludge concentration in the system, this value will be inversely proportional to the rate of increase of the sludge as determined by the nutrients available per floc, or expressed in more practical terms, the load per unit amount of sludge. It is usually calculated as:

$$\text{"Sludge Age" (days)} = \frac{\text{lb dry weight of activated sludge in the system}}{\text{lb dry weight of suspended solids entering the system per day}}$$

This value, although not the average age of the flocs, is proportional to it and is a useful guide to the efficiency of a sludge. The above definition supposes that the increase in sludge is proportional to the suspended solids load; whilst this may be a practical approximation with such wastes as domestic sewage, with other wastes having a higher proportion of the load in solution, the B.O.D. loading would be a more accurate basis for calculation, as suggested by Haseltine (1956).

A consideration of the mechanism of waste removal by activated sludge also shows the necessity of maintaining an ecological balance between food and microbial population—i.e. between load and the amount of sludge—in the plant. Although the organic waste is rapidly removed by the floc, the subsequent oxidation and synthesis of the transferred waste may take place over a longer period. For efficient operation, although oxidation of the waste may lag behind the removal, it must keep pace with it. Experience has shown that if the rate of removal exceeds that of oxidation, the sludge becomes difficult to settle and "bulking" results (Haseltine, 1956); in addition its powers of removing more waste become impaired. Work by the Water Pollution Research Laboratory (1956a), showed that by repeatedly aerating an activated sludge with sewage for half an hour and replacing the supernatant liquor, after settlement, with more sewage, the clarifying power of the sludge decreased rapidly with successive batches. When aerated for periods of an hour or more there was no loss of clarifying power.

A further increase in the difference between the rate of removal and metabolism of the waste, however, results in a sludge having good settling properties although its powers of waste removal are still impaired. This is probably the condition in the high rate activated sludge systems where rapid removal rates rather than high quality effluents are called for. In a conventional system, however, the floc should not be loaded with waste greatly in excess of that which it can oxidize in the aeration period provided. At a given flow this aeration period is largely predetermined by the tank capacity, but the sludge loading—

$$\frac{\text{Waste load (lb B.O.D. or S.S. per day)}}{\text{Amount of sludge in the system}}$$

—can be adjusted by changing the concentration of sludge in the system by controlled wastage over the excess sludge weir.

It will be seen that these two ecological considerations expressed in practice as "sludge age" and "sludge loading" are determined by the same factors and are mathematically the reciprocals of each other. Thus the general usage of "sludge age" as an operational guide in plant operation is ecologically sound.

Having accepted the principle of "sludge age" as a practical operational variable it becomes necessary to establish the optimum sludge age. In doing so it is necessary to consider both the activity of the floc and its settling properties. For optimum activity the flocs should be in the log phase of growth. A very young floc, however, although in the log phase, may be poorly flocculated and result in difficulties in separation from the purified liquor. On the other hand an aged floc, many of the bacteria in which may be in the endogenous phase, is less active. The optimum age will, therefore, lie somewhere between these extremes.

The settleability of sludges is measured by the "sludge index"; two such indexes are in common use. The sludge volume index (the Mohlman Index) is defined as the volume of sludge occupied by 1g (dry weight) of the sludge after 30 min quiescent settlement in a measuring cylinder. It is calculated thus:

$$\text{Sludge Volume Index} = \frac{\text{Settled volume of sludge percent after 30 min}}{\text{Suspended solids percent}}$$

For example, with a mixed liquor concentrate of 2000 ppm solids, the sludge in which occupies 20 per cent of the volume after 30 min settlement, this index would be

$$\frac{20}{0 \cdot 2} = 100$$

The same settling properties may also be expressed as the percentage of solids in the settled volume of sludge; this is known as the sludge density index (The Donaldson Index) and is given by—

$$\text{Sludge Density Index} = \frac{\text{Percent. suspended solid mixed liquor}}{\text{Percent. volume settled after 30 min}} \times 100$$

For the example taken above this would be—  $100 \times \dfrac{0 \cdot 2}{20} = 1$

It will be noticed that—

$$\text{Donaldson Index} = \frac{100}{\text{Mohlman Index}}$$

Reported American operational experiences show that there is a functional relationship between the sludge index and sludge age or sludge loading. In a conventional plant 3–4 days would appear to be the optimum age, whilst in high rate processes the age should be $0 \cdot 2$ days in hot weather and $0 \cdot 4$ days in cold (Edwards, 1949) (Gould, 1953). Within both these ranges, the sludge indexes should be satisfactory, i.e. the sludge volume index $< 100$. Between these ranges, however ($0 \cdot 5$ days–3 days), a high volume index may result. With a sludge age above 5–6 days, although most of the sludge comprises small dense flocs with a low index, some is present in the form of small flocs, known as pin-point flocs, which do not readily settle. Torpey and Chasick (1956), on the basis of experience at several New York plants, found that the optimum age was 3–4 days for most conventional plants. With high rate processes a range of $0 \cdot 2$–$0 \cdot 5$ day was found to be most satisfactory. Other workers have expressed the same relationship in terms of sludge loading. Haseltine (1956) concluded that the maximum B.O.D. load should not exceed $0 \cdot 5$ 1b per day per 1 lb of mixed liquor solids and suggests that in practice an average figure of $0 \cdot 3$–$0 \cdot 4$ lb for larger plants and $0 \cdot 2$–$0 \cdot 3$ lb for smaller plants having less attention. Logan and Budd (1956) quoted corresponding figures of $0 \cdot 22$–$0 \cdot 38$ lb as being necessary to ensure a sludge volume index of less than 100 in their pilot plant: above and below this range the sludge volume index increased. They also found that the optimum range decreased with increasing temperature and, therefore, more critical operational control was required at higher temperatures. They also produced evidence suggesting that there was a lag of 4–6 days between a specific loading and the resultant effect on the sludge index. Orford *et al.* (1960) found, using laboratory scale plants, that a loading of $0 \cdot 17$ lb B.O.D. per lb of volatile solids per day was optimum, above and below this figure the sludge volume index increased. In high rate activated sludge processes where use is made of the increased sludge density at low sludge ages ($0 \cdot 2$–$0 \cdot 4$ days) Haseltine (1956) recommends that the corresponding

B.O.D. loading should not be less than 1 lb per day per 1 lb of sludge, to minimize the chance of bulking. Such high rate processes do not always produce a clarified effluent and Gould and others (1960) state that they may not be equally effective with all wastes especially those having a high proportion of waste in solution.

As important as sludge loading is in relation to the settleability of the sludge, other factors may also cause bulking. Filamentous growths which are associated with a bulking condition, and are probably responsible for it, are encouraged by such environmental factors as acidity, low oxygen concentrations or nutrient unbalance. Again, sludge may rise in the settlement tanks due to the evolution of nitrogen gas liberated by the reduction of nitrates under anaerobic conditions.

Having determined the range within which it is desirable to maintain the sludge age and sludge loading, it is now necessary to consider how these can be satisfactorily achieved in practice. For a given B.O.D. load entering a conventional plant of fixed capacity, the sludge age can only be controlled by varying the aeration solids concentration. The maximum concentration of sludge in the aeration tanks of a conventional plant is limited by the speed at which it can be separated in the settling tanks and returned to the aeration tanks. As mentioned in the previous section on aeration, undue retention of the sludge in the settling tanks should normally be avoided. This retention time is determined by the amount of sludge entering the tanks, its settleability as measured by the sludge index, and the capacity of the pumps and hydraulics of the return sludge pipework. For a given retention time the concentration of the returned sludge is proportional to the sludge index at a constant rate of pumping. A longer retention time will, other things being equal, result in a higher concentration of returned sludge. Thus the relationship between the sludge index and the concentration of the returned sludge provides a useful guide to the retention time of the sludge in the settling tanks. Bloodgood considered that the percent concentration of returned sludge should never exceed the sludge density index if undue retention of the sludge were to be avoided. Thus for a sludge density index of 0·5 the return sludge concentration should not exceed 5000 ppm. Later (1944), the same worker reported that the percent concentration of returned sludge could be permitted to be 1·1 times the sludge density index, a concentration of 5500 ppm being permissible in the example quoted above.

In design therefore, not only should provision be made to accommodate the amount of sludge necessary to provide a satisfactory sludge age, but also for the expeditious removal and return of the sludge from the settling tanks. Such a system should be designed to operate under conditions of daily peak loadings and not daily average loadings, since most plants have to cope with daily fluctuations in strength and volume resulting  not only in variations in the sludge index, but with the distribution of the sludge throughout the system. A plant producing a high quality effluent for 22 hours each day may daily produce an unsatisfactory effluent for the other two hours following peak flows, due to the discharge of sludge in the effluent.

The permissible loading of a conventional plant is limited by the amount of sludge it can successfully carry in the aeration tanks without causing undue retention of the sludge in the settling tanks. Although the provision of a generous sludge return does not affect the average waste aeration period it inevitably increases the flow through the settling tanks. Haseltine (1956) however, considered that, providing that the sludge is withdrawn from a point immediately below the tank inlet, this should not necessitate an increase in tank capacity. Many of the modified methods of operation are aimed at overcoming the above limitations of the settlement stage. By arranging for progressive mixing of the waste with the returned sludge throughout the aeration tank, it is possible to carry the necessary amount of sludge in the aeration tanks and yet ensure that the concentration entering the settling tanks is not excessive. In "step aeration" where the waste is introduced at stages along the aeration channel, a higher concentration of sludge is held under aeration at the inlet end than at the outlet end, thus reducing the concentration passing to the settling tanks (Torpey and Chasick, 1956). The higher the proportion of the load applied away from the inlet end, the greater this effect, the extreme case being where no waste is added to the first sections of the aeration tank; this corresponds to the practice of "sludge re-aeration" or "sludge reconditioning". The flexibility of step aeration, however, whereby the proportion of waste applied at each stage can be varied to meet fluctuations in the load, is superior to the fixed capacity sludge re-conditioning tanks. The practice of re-aeration, with reduced periods of mixed liquor retention times, is possible because of the fairly rapid uptake of the waste by the sludge and its continued metabolism in the re-aeration tanks. On this principle the time of retention of the waste liquor in the aeration  tanks is not critical, providing that it is sufficient to permit the complete  transfer of the waste to the sludge. A period of two hours should normally be adequate. Thus plant design based on the need to provide for the accommodation and recycling of the requisite microbial population, needed to balance the waste load to ensure optimum sludge conditions, is ecologically more sound than the more conventional design criteria involving the provision of tank capacity to ensure a given aeration contact time of the mixed liquor.

Other systems have been developed to ensure a more uniform loading of the flocs during their retention in the aeration tank. A high rate of sludge return itself tends to provide more uniform loading. In the Logan process some aeration tank effluent is returned to the inlet end of the tanks together with the returned sludge. The flow of returned mixed liquor is approximately 3–4 times that of the waste (Busch and Kalinske, 1956). Complete uniformity of loading is probably achieved in the complete mixing systems. Conditions in a conventional aeration tank, as opposed to an aeration channel, probably more nearly approach complete mixing of waste and sludge than is generally realized. An unconventional plant, described by Busch and Kalinske (1956), was designed to meet the several ecological requirements discussed above. The processes of aeration and settlement are carried out in the one tank. The completely mixed waste and sludge are subjected to conditions of intense agitation in a central zone whilst quiescent settlement takes place in an upper outer zone, separated from the aeration zone by a hood. The sludge settling in the quiescent zone is rapidly carried back beneath the hood by the recirculating mixed liquor.

In plant design also, provision should be made for the acceptance and treatment of the excess sludge in varying amounts according to the operational requirements of the aeration unit. The situation should never arise where the sludge concentration in the aeration unit cannot be reduced because of lack of capacity in the sludge treatment plant. Because of the sensitivity of activated sludge to fluctuations in load, all efforts should be made to control the discharge of strong liquors from the digestion plant to avoid increasing the normal fluctuations in load. In some cases separate treatment of such liquors could be practised with advantage as in the Kraus process (Kraus, 1945).

In the foregoing discussion the efficiency of the activated sludge

10

system has been considered in terms of carbonaceous oxidation. Activated sludge is capable of nitrification under suitable conditions of operation. Unfortunately it would appear that loading conditions needed for nitrification are not the optimum conditions for maintaining a satisfactory sludge. Nitrification is usually associated with a lightly loaded sludge, i.e. one having a high sludge age. Autotrophic nitrifying organisms have a relatively slow rate of multiplication and could hardly be expected to become established in a floc of low sludge age. Also, in competition with the more rapidly growing heterotrophic organisms, they would be less likely to succeed in a heavily loaded floc. Such underloaded sludges in which oxidation exceeds waste uptake do not produce clear effluents (Haseltine, 1956). Although the flocs are dense and settle well, large numbers of pin-point flocs do not settle and are discharged with the effluent.

*Microscopical Examination as an Operational Aid*

In practice the autecological conditions within the plant can be checked by routine tests to determine the temperature, pH, dissolved oxygen concentration, etc. The synecological balance between load and microbial population can be maintained by adjustments based on frequent determinations of the flow and strength of the waste feed and the concentration of the sludge in the system. Sludge index determinations will act as a check on the resultant settleability. The return sludge concentration in relation to the sludge density index should prove a useful guide to the sludge retention time in the settling tanks, as described above. If the necessary capacity and operational flexibility has been provided for in the plant design, the operator using the results of these tests, should be able to maintain the sludge in a healthy efficient condition. Direct microscopical examination of the sludge will reveal to what extent he has succeeded. Frequent regular observations will indicate trends in sludge conditions and can be used as a supplementary guide in plant operation.

It cannot be overstressed that the nature of the sludge and its component populations will depend upon the nature of the waste being treated. Even under otherwise identical operating conditions, plants treating different wastes will have sludges of different appearance and containing different organisms. Conversely plants treating the same waste under slightly different operating conditions may form sludges of markedly different natures (Plate a and c). It follows therefore, that only by experience gained by continued acquaintanceship with the sludge in his plant and by the application of general principles can an operator make full use of microscopical observations.

Some criteria which have been found useful in assessing the condition of sludges treating sewage may be given as a guide as to what features to look for in routine observations. Such observations are best made on the sludge removed from the outlet end of the aeration tanks and with the minimum of delay after removal. The size, shape, structure of the individual flocs and the relative sizes of the different flocs are important features. Large tassel-like flocs (Plate c) although having fair settling qualities have been associated with a less efficient sludge than smaller flocs of more open texture (Plate). The flocs should be well-defined with no dispersed solids in the interstitial liquor. Examination of the floc margin under the high power of the microscope will reveal the degree of flocculation of the bacteria. In some cases the bacteria will be seen to be firmly embedded in the floc which then has a sharply defined margin. Under other conditions the bacteria are only loosely associated at the surface of the floc giving it a diffuse margin. Bacteria in such flocs are in a young active state and are capable of rapid oxidation of the waste. A slight increase in load, however, causes them to disperse into the interstitial liquid thus producing a turbid inferior effluent, even though the waste may have been completely removed. Filamentous growths such as *Sphaerotilus* and fungi, whether the causative organisms or not, are often associated with chronic bulking of sludges. Microscopical examination will reveal the appearance and development of such growths before serious bulking occurs and thus enable remedial action to be taken.

Independent of any role they may play in the process, protozoa have been proved by experience to be of great value as indicator organisms. It is, however, dangerous to apply "rule of thumb" methods when using any such indicators, but with a knowledge of the dominant species present in his plant, an operator, working on the general principles of the succession of dominant groups with increased purification, should find routine microscopical examination of the sludge of great value. Although Reynoldson (1942a) found that there was a direct relationship between the numbers of vorticellids in the sludge and the

10*

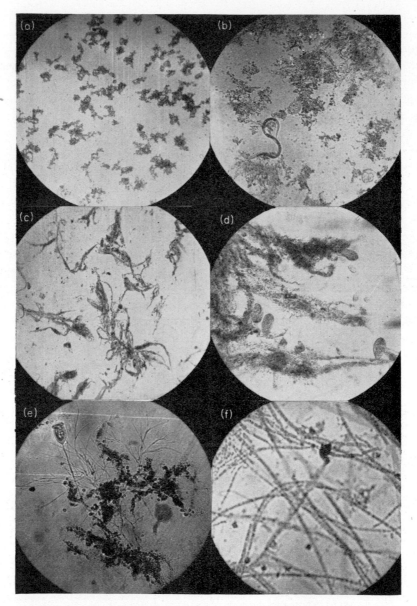

Plate 1. Photomicrographs of activated sludge.

(a) Typical appearance of flocs ($\times$ 15). (b) Flocs with *Vorticella* and *Nematode* worm ($\times$ 25). (c) Large tassel-like flocs associated with inferior conditions ($\times$ 15). (d) Tassel-like flocs, with free swimming ciliates. ($\times$ 45). (e) Flocs showing development bacterial filaments ($\times$ 80). (f) Filaments of *Sphaerotilus* ($\times$ 450).

quality of the effluent at Huddersfield, attempts to correlate the protozoa numbers with effluent quality at Birmingham showed that although
such a relationship was established over periods of several weeks, no
such correlation existed throughout the year; it was concluded that the
nature of the protozoa community was more indicative than were
specific numbers (Baines *et al.* 1953). As recently pointed out by McKinney and Gram (1956) no simple quantitative relationship could be
expected; for example, a decline in the free-swimming ciliates may
indicate either decreased or increased efficiency. A study of the whole
community, however, would tell whether this decline was associated
with an increase in the flagellates or attached ciliates and thus would
indicate the trend in efficiency. Experience at Coleshill (Birmingham)
has shown that some protozoa have a greater indicator value than others
and some exceptions to the generally accepted pattern have been observed.

Although most species of *Vorticella*, an attached ciliate, occur in an
efficient sludge together with *Opercularia*, *Aspidisca* and *Lionotus*, one
species, *V. microstoma*, is more common at times when the effluent is
inferior; it is also the dominant ciliate—usually the only one—in the
partial activated sludge plants at other Birmingham works, its incidence
there being more associated with the toxicity of the industrial sewages.
*Paramoecium caudatum*, usually associated with a less efficient sludge, has
at times been present in large numbers when the effluent was good,
but its numbers fluctuate violently. A species of *Arcella*, a rhizopod
(a group quoted as indicative of inefficient sludges), has usually been
found associated with the high-quality nitrified effluents.

In quoting these exceptions, it is not intended to detract from the
usefulness of protozoa as indicators, but merely to warn against over-
rigid application of the general principle. The type of protozoan community is determined by the interaction of several factors such as the
dissolved oxygen concentration, the concentration of organic matter
and the bacterial flora and thus reflects the general conditions within
the plant and not merely sludge efficiency. It should also be pointed
out that the protozoan population is affected by the state of purification of the waste and, as in the case of a light or bulking sludge,
the effluent may contain microbial masses, the presence of which results
in inferior-quality effluents, this not being reflected by the protozoa.
Of the other higher micro-organisms occurring in sludges, rotifers
usually indicate better conditions than do the nematode worms.

# CHAPTER 6

# THE ECOLOGICAL CONTROL
# OF POPULATIONS AND ACTIVITY
# IN BACTERIA BEDS

As with activated sludge, a pre-requisite of the process is the intimate contact of the waste with an active microbial population in the presence of oxygen. In bacteria beds, however, this is achieved in a different manner by allowing the waste to flow over the micro-organisms exposed as a zöogleal film on the bed medium, the oxygen mostly being provided by the air currents through the bed. The biophysical and biochemical processes bringing about the waste removal and its oxidation are probably similar to those operative in activated sludge. Bacteria-bed film has been credited with phenomenally high instantaneous rates of oxidation in keeping with the rapid removal of B.O.D. during the relatively short retention time of the liquor in the bed. The relative instantaneous rates of removal and oxidation will probably depend upon the nature of the waste. With wastes having the organic matter in solution and in such concentrations that they are limiting the growth rate of the micro-organisms, the organic matter could be expected to be utilized as it is removed. With stronger soluble wastes some may be stored as reserves such as glycogen within the cells for subsequent oxidation. With wastes having organic matter as suspended or colloidal solids, these readily flocculate on the surface of the film and may only be absorbed slowly, prior to oxidation. The period of contact, the liquid retention time, should be sufficient to ensure the transfer of the waste to the film by adsorption or absorption for subsequent oxidation. To avoid the progressive accumulation of unoxidized waste in the bed, the overall rate of oxidation of the waste must equal the rate of removal of the waste. In other words the amount of waste, the oxidation of which is completed per day, should equal the amount of waste removed per day. This does not imply that the time needed for oxidation is the same as that required for the initial removal of the waste. There is no functional relationship between the liquid contact time—the time required for the removal of the waste—and the instantaneous rate of oxidation of the removed waste. As an analogy we may consider the routine in a laboratory regularly receiving 100 samples for B.O.D. determinations each day. Although the time needed to perform the test on 100 samples is 5 days, the overall rate of obtaining results is the same as that of the reception of samples—100 per day. The 100 samples received per day represent the waste removed in unit time in the bed, the 5 day incubation period of the test represents, conveniently enough, the period between removal of the waste and the completion of its oxidation. The 100 results represent the amount of waste, the oxidation of which is completed each above-mentioned unit of time. The 500 samples in the incubator represent the amount of waste stored or under oxidation in the bed. The analogy may be safely carried a step further. If the number of samples were increased to 120 per day, then, after a 5 day period, the number of results—or tests completed, would be 120 per day provided that two conditions were fulfilled. Firstly the capacity of the incubator must be adequate to accommodate the increased number of samples being incubated—600, and secondly, the laboratory staff, by increasing its activity or numbers, must be capable of dealing with the extra samples. Similarly, in a bacteria bed a 20 per cent increase in the load of removed waste could be dealt with provided that the film was able to accommodate the resultant increased storage matter without impairing its efficiency and secondly the micro-organisms were able to increase their activity or population to deal with the increased food supply. These considerations point to two factors limiting the loading of bacteria beds; the extent to which they can accommodate the unoxidized removed waste without impairing the efficiency of the film, and the size of the microbial population that the bed can effectively support. In addition, of course, the effect of the increased load on the initial removal must also be considered.

The instantaneous rate of oxidation is a function of the concentration of the substrate, thus the high rates of oxidation associated with the bacteria-bed film may be due to the concentration of the waste at the surface of the film due to the physical forces associated with interfaces. The amount of unoxidized organic matter in a bed will depend upon the speed of oxidation. If the speed is halved the amount of unoxidized matter is doubled but providing that the film can accommodate this increase and the microbial population deal with it, the total amount oxidized per day will be the same, for although the instantaneous rate of oxidation is halved the amount available for oxidation is doubled. Thus a new balance is established. Below 50°F although the initial removal rate in bacteria beds is probably not affected, the instantaneous rate of oxidation probably is. In beds treating wastes having a high proportion of suspended or colloidal matter, this may result in an excessive accumulation of unoxidized flocculated solids in the film. This resultant increase in film accumulation at low temperatures should be distinguished from that due to the increase in microbial mass, for reasons already discussed.

As with activated sludge it is necessary to maintain an active population of heterotrophic micro-organisms and in a bacteria bed this can only be achieved by preventing excessive overgrowth of the film. There is normally a seasonal decline in the efficiency of beds during the winter, in contrast with the activated sludge process. We have seen that there is usually more film present in the beds during the winter than in the summer. The extent to which the decreased efficiency is due to lower temperatures or increased film is difficult to assess. *Figure* 6.1. shows the seasonal fluctuations in film accumulation, temperature and efficiency of two beds, one in which the usual accumulation of film occurred in the winter and the other in which it was suppressed by controlled frequency of dosing. It will be seen that the efficiency of the bed in which there was no winter accumulation of film showed little seasonal fluctuation compared with that in the bed in which winter film accumulation occurred. Although not eliminating temperature as a factor, these results do confirm that film accumulation itself is an important factor.

Whilst most workers agree on the desirability of preventing excessive accumulations of film, there would appear to be some difference of opinion as to the optimum amount needed. Some consider that as thick a growth as possible, compatible with the prevention of ponding and ensuring the adequate aeration of the bed, is desirable (Taylor, 1957). Lloyd (1945) considered that were it not for the increased metabolic activity of the micro-organisms at higher temperatures in the summer, their reduced numbers, due to the dominance of the grazing fauna, could result in decreased purification. Experience with beds at different works, however, has led me to believe that a very thin film indeed, perceptible only to the touch as a slime on the stones, is all

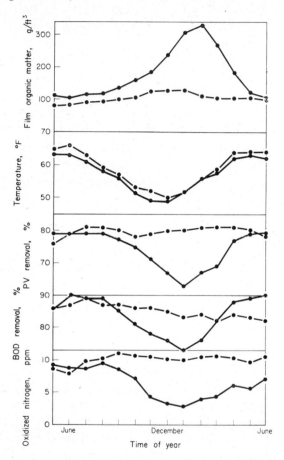

FIG. 6.1. Comparison of the seasonal fluctuation in efficiency of two bacteria beds. (The full line is for a filter in which film accumulated and the broken line is for a filter in which film was controlled by low frequency dosing).

that is necessary for efficient purification. This view is supported by experimental evidence (*Water Pollution Research* 1957). Using inclined rotating tubes (Gloyna *et al.* 1952) it was found that the maximum efficiency of removal of organic carbon was reached when a film of only $0 \cdot 12$ mm average thickness was formed. Wuhrmann (1960) calculated that the thickness of film in which all the bacteria could be expected to receive adequate oxygen supply, as being $100$–$200\mu$ ($0 \cdot 1$–$0 \cdot 2$ mm). Thus although the amount of film which can be accommodated in a unit volume of bed, without causing ponding or impeding aeration, is limited by the void capacity between the media, the amount of active film is limited by the total surface area of the stones on which the thin film can be supported.

Although only a thin bacterial film is considered necessary for efficient purification, the thickness at which its activity per unit area is impaired is more difficult to establish in practice. As a rough guide, considering medium of nominal size ($1\frac{1}{2}$ in), the volatile solids should probably not exceed 50g dry weight per cubic foot of bed, possibly less if nitrification is desired. When the growth is dominated by certain fungi, such as *Ascoidea* which forms foam-like masses filling the interstices, larger amounts—up to 200g dry weight volatile matter per cubic foot—may be maintained in a healthy aerobic condition. Although such growths render the bed highly efficient, unless they are controlled they eventually result in ponding with marked decrease in efficiency (Hawkes, 1957). Such growths have been experienced within beds operating on A.D.F. Other fungi such as *Fusarium* and *Geotrichum* are, like bacteria, more closely associated with the surface of the stones.

Consideration must also be given to the vertical distribution throughout the depth of the bed. In conventional beds, because of the reduction in concentration of the waste during purification as it passes downwards, most growth occurs at or near the surface. Although at times when such surface growths are sufficient to reduce the efficiency of the affected uppermost part of the bed, the film within the bed may still be in the active log phase. The surface growths, however, may cause ponding which interferes with the distribution of the waste and the aeration of the bed, thus affecting the efficiency of the whole bed. Furthermore, because of the reduction in efficiency of the upper portion of the bed, the film below receives a higher concentration of the waste, thereby increasing the growth rate of the organisms. Thus a downward growth of the film takes place, the efficient portion of the bed being successively reduced and the nitrification zone lowered or even eliminated. During the unloading of the film the reverse probably occurs, the lower accumulation of solids being discharged first.

Bacteria beds must not only be operated efficiently but also without causing nuisance. Flies, such as *Psychoda* spp. and *Anisopus fenestralis*, have caused serious nuisance in the vicinity of bacteria beds. Synthetic insecticides are being used successfully to control these flies but such a practice, although under many conditions necessary as a palliative measure, is ecologically unsound. The occasional application of insecticide results in a reduction in the insect population causing an upset in the ecological balance which may result in a rapid increase in film which is then available to support an increased fly population necessitating further applications of insecticide (Hawkes, 1952). It is possible by successive applications of insecticide to change the fauna of a bed from one dominated by flies to one having less troublesome organisms such as *Achorutes* or *Lumbricillid* worms as the dominant members (Hawkes, 1955a). Such a balance can, however, only be maintained by expensive insecticide treatments and when these are suspended the normal fauna is rapidly re-established. A further objection to the use of insecticides on bacteria beds is the danger of discharging a toxic effluent.

In more natural environments the factors controlling animal populations are still not fully understood, but in bacteria beds food supply is a most important factor (Hawkes, 1952). The soundest way to control a fly population breeding in bacteria beds, therefore, is by controlling their food supply, i.e. limiting the accumulation of film. Thus, for optimum efficiency and prevention of nuisance, the limitation of film accumulation is desirable. The control of the microbial population, necessary for efficient operation and prevention of nuisance, cannot be directly effected by such mechanical operations as adjusting the excess sludge weir as in the activated sludge plant. It can only be achieved indirectly through biological agencies by the ecological control of the competing populations. Factors influencing this balance of populations have previously been discussed and it now remains to be considered by which of the factors the desirable level of population can best be maintained.

PRACTICAL METHODS OF MAINTAINING
THE BALANCE OF POPULATIONS AT A
LOW LEVEL

The rate of film accumulation may be considered as a function of the rate of growth and rate of removal.

$$(R_a) \qquad = \qquad (R_g) \qquad - \qquad (R_r)$$

*Rate of accumulation*     *Rate of growth*     *Rate of removal*

To maintain $R_a$ at zero, i.e. to prevent accumulation, two theoretical alternatives are possible. One method would be to operate the bed to encourage maximum growth—i.e. $R_g$ is a maximum—for the waste being treated, and maintain conditions so that $R_r = R_g$. The alternative would be to limit the growth rate $R_g$ by operational means so that $R_g$ equals $R_r$ under the operating conditions imposed. The two alternatives are thus basically different and are, as we shall see, in some ways incompatible.

Of the two possible approaches, the former, whereby maximum growth rate and activity of the film are encouraged, but the accumulation of film is maintained at a low level by a dominant grazing fauna, is preferable. The resultant low level of the film accumulation would cause severe competition for the limited food among the grazing fauna. In insect populations the percentage number of larvae which successfully pupate, before emerging as adults, decreases with decreasing food supply when the latter is limiting. Thus under conditions of limiting food supply, much of the available food is wasted to the fly population by the death at different stages of development of larvae which have used some of the available food. This phenomenon, known ecologically as a "scramble", is attractive as a method of utilizing the benefits of an insect population without incurring the nuisance of a large adult population. It is a self-regulating mechanism in that the fewer eggs produced by the reduced adult fly population would result in a reduced larval population with less severe competition and a resultant lower death rate.

Unfortunately, it is only in beds treating a weak waste with resultant low growth rate $-(R_g)$ that conditions suitable to support this balance can be maintained throughout the year. In other beds, although at summer temperatures such conditions may prevail, the lower winter temperatures result in the accumulation of film for reasons previously discussed. If the rate of accumulation is slight, it may be that the resultant accumulation throughout the winter is not sufficient to affect the efficiency of the bed before the spring unloading takes place. In more heavily loaded beds, or those subjected to lower temperatures, the greater accumulation of film results in decreased efficiency. In both, the unloading in the spring, usually brought about by an increased grazing population, uncontrolled by the available food, is associated with a potential fly nuisance. Also, by permitting this winter accumulation of film, the increased rate of discharge of humus sludge during the resultant spring unloading, imposes an increased load on the digestion plant, often when it is least able to cope with it. These effects of low winter temperatures could be overcome by heating the beds either directly or by heating the feed liquor. Fuel for this could be provided by the gas from the digestion of sludge. Alternatively in the vicinity of generating stations, cooling water could be used.

In many beds, because of the nature and strength of the waste and the economic necessity of operating at higher rates, the grazing fauna is not able to dominate the film, especially in the winter, and in such cases it is necessary to adopt the second alternative and control the growth rate $(R_g)$. Of the advantages claimed for the modified methods of filtration commonly practised, such as recirculation, alternating double filtration, and low frequency dosing, the control of film accumulation is common to all. The method by which this is achieved, however, has been variously described; some consider that the flushing action resulting from the higher rate of instantaneous application is the cause, others consider that nutritional control is the operative factor. In the light of results reported above, it is considered that flushing action can have little effect in removing attached film from within the bed at the usual rates of application practised in this country. An understanding of the controlling mechanism is not only of academic interest but is essential for its successful application and for the diagnosis of the cause of failure should this occur. We shall, therefore, now consider these different methods of "filtration" as film controlling processes, although in doing so their other advantages should not be overlooked.

*Recirculation*

Ecologically the most important features of recirculation, whereby the waste is diluted with returned effluent before being applied to the bed, are the reduction in strength of feed and the increase in the hydraulic load. As shown in *Fig.* 6.2, these two factors influence the growth rate of the film and its vertical distribution throughout the depth of the bed. Applying the growth rate/concentration curve discussed earlier, a waste having a concentration $C_1$ gives an arbitrary growth rate $R_1$ on the surface of the bed operating as a single filter. By introducing recirculation and thereby reducing the concentration of the feed to $C_2$ the resultant growth rate is reduced to $R_2$. Consider now the growth rate within the bed, say at a depth of 2 ft. With single filtration suppose the initial waste concentration $C_1$ has been reduced to $C_3$ giving a reduced growth rate $R_3$. With recirculation because of the higher hydraulic loading the reduction in concentration in the upper 2 ft of bed is less than with single filtration and the resultant concentration $C_4$ may well be higher than the concentration $C_3$ at the corresponding depth in the bed operating by single filtration, as indeed was found to be the case by Lumb and Eastwood (1958). As a result, the growth rate of the film at a depth of 2 ft within a recirculating bed is greater than in a conventional bed. These results would account for the reduction in amounts of surface film and the more even vertical distribution of the film throughout the depth of the bed with recirculation. A greater depth of the bed is thus used for carbonaceous oxidation but the zone of nitrification is restricted.

To effect this reduction in film growth at the surface it is essential that the dilution of the feed is sufficient to result in a concentration which falls on the slope of the growth rate curve, i.e. a concentration at which nutrient is limiting. It could be that with a strong waste $C_5$, and a low dilution ratio, the resultant diluted feed $C_6$ would have the same growth rate—$R_{5,6}$ at the surface of the bed, the concentration of the feed $C_6$ not being growth controlling. Furthermore, because of the resultant greater hydraulic loading it is possible that the accumulation of film will also occur to a greater depth than with single filtration.

To control film growth nutritionally in beds treating fluctuating flows, the dilution ratio should ideally be constant, i.e. the recircula-

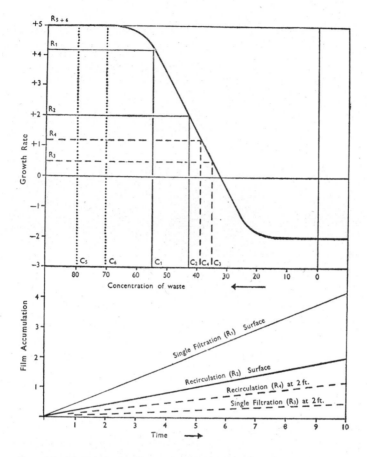

FIG. 6.2. Theoretical effect of recirculation on the growth rate of film at different depths in a bacteria bed. (Reproduced from Hawkes, H.A. (1961). An ecological approach to some bacteria bed problems *J. Inst. Sewage Purif.*, (2) by kind permission of the editor).

tion rate varied directly with the flow of waste. Lumb and Eastwood (1958) compared different applications of recirculation to beds treating fluctuating sewage flows. On the bed in which the recirculation rate was varied directly with the sewage flow to maintain a constant dilution ratio, there was little ponding. On a second bed, however, in which the recirculation rate varied inversely with the sewage flow, to maintain a constant flow to the bed, severe ponding occurred in the winter period (*Fig.* 6.3).

The operation of the former ideal method of recirculation involves plant of larger capacity and variable pumping capacity with the neces-

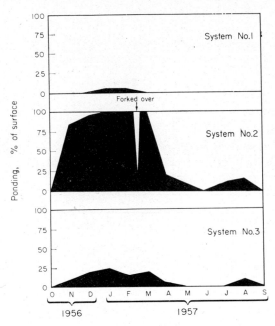

FIG. 6.3.   Degrees of ponding with different systems of recirculation.

  I Rate of recirculation varying directly with rate of sewage inflow.
 II Rate of recirculation varying inversely with rate of sewage inflow.
III Rate of recirculation constant.
    Reproduced from Lumb. C. (1960) The application of recircu-
lation to the purification of sewage and trade wastes, *Waste
Treatment* (Ed. P.C.G. Isaac), Pergamon Press, Oxford, 195.
by kind permission of author and editor.

sary control mechanism. A third method investigated by Lumb and Eastwood, whereby a constant recirculation rate calculated to give an average dilution ratio equal to the ideal system was maintained irrespective of the sewage flow, proved only slightly inferior to the ideal (*Fig.* 6.3). Plant capacity is not as great as in the ideal system and pumping plant and control gear is the simplest of the three methods. The degree of dilution of the feed depends not only upon the dilution ratio but also on the quality of the diluting effluent. Thus, if for any reason the efficiency of the bed falls off, normal recirculation will be less effective in controlling film, and further deterioration in conditions may result. By diluting the feed with purified effluent from a more efficient bed or activated sludge plant it is possible that further deterioration would be prevented (Lumb, 1956). Besides this effect of the growth rate ($R_g$) recirculation may also affect the removal rate ($R_r$) by changing the numbers and species of grazing fauna. The increased hydraulic rate of application tends to reduce the numbers of fly larvae such as *Psychoda* and the Springtails such as *Achorutes*. The more prehensile *Lumbricillid* worms persist and with the reduced interspecific competition they may increase in numbers. Such a change in fauna has been reported by Lumb and Eastwood (1958) and by Hawkes (1961). There were indications that the *Lumbricillid* worms were less active in removing film than the *Psychoda* population they had replaced.

*Alternating Double Filtration (A.D.F.)*

The process of A.D.F., in which waste is treated on a pair of beds in series, each bed alternately becoming primary and secondary in successive periods, was first conceived by O'Shaughnessy (1931) as a means of controlling excessive film growth. He had observed that excessive accumulations on beds could be removed by applying the effluent from a bioflocculation plant. Thus, from the beginning it was acknowledged that the control of film was an important feature of A.D.F. Tomlinson (1941) later demonstrated that this was due to a starvation effect during the secondary stage of the process during which the film decreased in amount. This is also explicable in terms of the growth curve (*Fig.* 6.4). During the primary stage the growth rate ($R_1$) at the surface is determined by the concentration $C_1$ of the waste, and is the same as that on the surface of a conventional bed treating the same waste. During the secondary stage the film is subjected to the settled primary bed effluent of concentration $C_2$ giving a negative growth rate $R_2$. Thus the resultant growth rate $\dfrac{R_1 + R_2}{2}$ is less than $R_1$, the rate at the surface of a conventional bed. Because of the higher hydraulic loading the film is distributed more evenly throughout the depth of the bed as in recirculation. The total amount

11

of film, however, is less than in single beds treating the same waste since with A.D.F. all the film is subjected to the negative growth phase in the secondary stage, whereas in a conventional bed the bulk of the film in the upper layers of the bed is normally never subjected to starvation conditions and the resultant negative growth rate. Thus, this principle of A.D.F. is based on a fundamentally sound theoretical basis. The process has been successfully applied to the treatment of sewage at Reading (Barraclough, 1954) and Derby (Greene, 1957) and has proved of particular value in treating wastes, such as those from milk processing, which tend to give rise to fungal growths (*Water Pollution Research*, Technical paper No. 8, 1941).

Experience at Birmingham, where the successful development of the process by the Water Pollution Research Laboratory (Wishart and Wilkinson, 1941) (Mills, 1945) led to it being adopted for large scale operation (Daviss, 1951), has shown that to be successful the process must produce a primary effluent which will ensure that in the secondary stage the film is in the endogenous phase to produce a negative growth rate $(R_2)$. Even when this is achieved the resultant growth rate is positive and to prevent film accumulation this has to be countered by an equal removal rate $(R_r)$. In beds operating at conventional hydraulic loadings this is mostly provided by the activity of the grazing fauna. At times when this is reduced, as when temperatures are low, it is essential that the resultant growth rate is kept low by a negative growth rate in the secondary stage. If for any reason an inferior primary effluent is produced either because of reduced efficiency or higher loadings, the carbonaceous oxidation is continued in the secondary stage and the final effluent is at first little affected apart from the reduced nitrate content since nitrification is not similarly increased in the secondary stage. However, the higher nutrient concentration results in a positive growth rate in the secondary stage and an increase in the degree of film accumulation. This could result in a further decrease in efficiency and a further deterioration in the primary effluent. Thus conditions progressively deteriorate until the process eventually breaks down in the complete ponding of the beds. It was found that this adverse sequence of events could be prevented by applying a further growth-controlling factor—the frequency at which successive doses of sewage were applied to the bed.

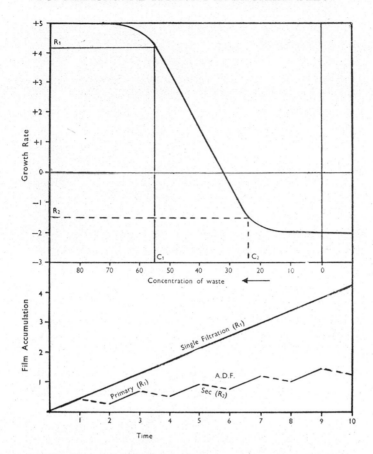

Fig. 6.4. Theoretical effect of alternating double filtration on the growth rate of film during the primary and secondary stages. (Reproduced from Hawkes, H.A., (1961). An ecological approach to some bacteria bed problems, *J. Inst. Sewage Purif.*, (2) by kind permission of the editor.

## Frequency of Dosing

At the same overall rate of treatment the waste may be applied as a continuous spray or as a succession of doses. The frequency at which these doses are applied may also vary, the lower the frequency the higher the instantaneous rate of application. This frequency of dosing is a most important ecological factor in the operation of bacteria beds.

11*

Early in the history of bacteria beds it was reported in evidence to the Royal Commission on Sewage Disposal (1908) that intermittent dosing of beds limited the accumulation of film. It is of interest to note that one of the first bacteria beds to be operated at the Lawrence Experiment Station, Massachusetts, in 1890 was dosed intermittently at 20 min intervals (Stanbridge, 1954). At Birmingham early in the century, one of the experimental beds was equipped with a one-armed distributor mechanically driven to rotate once every 7 min by means of a 2 h.p. oil engine.

Lumb and Barnes (1948) at Halifax found that by slowing down the speed of rotation of a four-armed distributor, the condition and performance of the bed was improved. Tomlinson and Hall (1955) investigated the effect of frequency of dosing on beds operating on A.D.F. They concluded that for four-armed distributors the optimum rate of rotation under their conditions of experiment was between 15 and 30 min per rev. During the later period of these investigations comparisons of the seasonal fluctuations in film accumulation and fauna in low and high frequency dosed beds were made (Hawkes, 1955). The results are summarized in *Fig.* 6.5. In the beds served with rapidly revolving self-propelled distributors there was, each winter, an excessive accumulation of film; in similar beds treating the same sewage at the same rate but having the distributors mechanically rotated at speeds between 30 and 55 min per rev, the amount of film was uniformly low. There was also a marked effect on the grazing fauna; the fly populations, both *Anisopus* and *Psychoda*, were almost eliminated in the low frequency dosed beds. This was partly due to the reduced food supply in the form of film and also to the greater downward rate of flow of the sewage suppressing the larvae populations within the bed. The more strongly prehensile *Lumbricillid* worms were better able to withstand the stronger flow of sewage and, in the absence of competition from the fly larvae, they became more abundant in the low frequency dosed beds. Thus, by reducing the frequency of dosing, ecological conditions were created which not only maintained a low degree of film accumulation necessary for efficient purification, but also prevented fly nuisance by changing the fauna from one dominated by flies to one dominated by worms.

For successful application of controlled frequency dosing it is essential to appreciate the principles underlying the process. Unfortunately, as in many developments of biological filtration where practice has led theory, the practical success has been explained by various theories. The resultant high instantaneous dosage rate is generally considered to be an important feature of the process. In view of the evidence reported earlier in this work, however, the scouring effect of this high

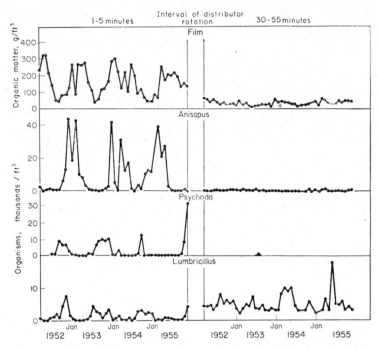

FIG. 6.5. Relative film accumulation and fauna population in two similar bacteria beds operating under conditions identical except for speed of rotation of distributor arms.

instantaneous rate cannot be considered to be an important factor in controlling film, especially within the bed, although it does affect the fauna, the fly larvae being replaced by the more strongly prehensile *Lumbricillid* worms. An alternative theory suggests that because of the infrequent application of waste, the film is subjected to reduced nutrient concentration, if not starvation conditions, for some of the period between doses. To investigate this nutritional effect, samples were taken at minute intervals from side arm sampling channels col-lecting the effluents at 1 ft, 3 ft and 5 ft depths of the bed to measure the change in concentration between doses at 15 min intervals as measured by the O.A. Similar samples from the same bed being dosed at $1\frac{1}{2}$ min intervals were taken on the next day. The results of both tests expressed as ppm O.A. remaining per 100 ppm. O.A. applied are shown in *Fig.* 6.6 Whereas only slight fluctuations in the strength of

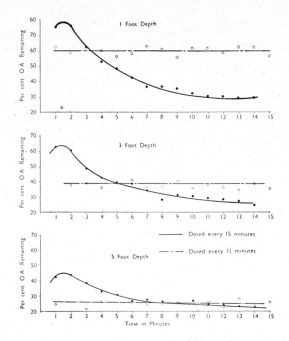

FIG. 6.6. Fluctuations in the strength of liquor between successive doses at 1 ft, 3 ft, and 5 ft, depths of a bacteria bed dosed at 15 min intervals, compared with those when the bed was dosed at $1\frac{1}{2}$ min intervals. (Reproduced from Hawkes, H.A. (1961) An ecological approach to some bacteria bed problems, *J. Inst. Sewage Purif.*, (2) by kind permission of the editor.

liquid occurred at any one depth with the rapidly revolving distributor, when the distributor revolved slowly there was a marked reduction in strength over the 15 min period between the doses, this being most marked at the 1 ft depth. Applying these results to the conventional growth rate curve (*Fig.* 6.7) it is seen that at the 1 ft level, for more than two-thirds of the time the growth rate with low frequency dosing is considerably less than with high frequency dosing and may well pass into the endogenous phase towards the end of the period between doses. Within the bed at a depth of 3 ft for half the time the growth rate would be higher with high frequency dosing, although at 5 ft

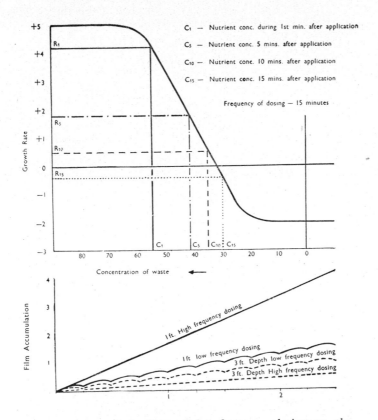

FIG. 6.7. Theoretical effect of low-frequency dosing on the growth rate of film at different depths in a bacteria bed (Reproduced from Hawkes, H.A. (1961) An ecological approach to some bacteria bed problems, *J. Inst. Sewage Purif.*, (2) by kind permission of the editor.

the growth rate would be higher with low frequency dosing. This would account for the more even distribution of film throughout the depth of the bed with low frequency dosing (*Fig.* 3.3). The results illustrate that with low frequency dosing the average concentration of nutrients available to the film in the upper layers is reduced, thus reducing the growth rate (*Fig.* 6.7). Therefore the control of film in low frequency dosed beds could be accounted for by nutritional control as in recirculation and A.D.F.

Suggestions by Stanbridge (1956) that low frequency dosing may have advantages other than those attributable to the control of film

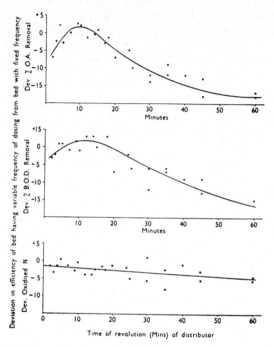

FIG. 6.8. Effect of frequency of dosing on the efficiency of a bacteria bed having only a low accumulation of film. (Reproduced from Hawkes, H.A. (1961) An ecological approach to some bacteria bed problems, *J. Inst. Sewage Purif.*, (2) by kind permission of the editor.

have been investigated (Hawkes, 1961). To investigate this possibility, use was made of a circular bed which had a distributor fitted with variable speed drive. On several daily occasions the distributor was revolved at different speeds between 1 rev in 3 min and 1 rev in 60 min, the speed on each occasion being chosen at random; the efficiency, as assessed by the percentage O.A. and B.O.D. removal and the amount of oxidized N in the effluents, was determined. On the same occasion the efficiency of a similar bed receiving the same sewage through distributors revolving at a fixed rate was measured. The differences between the efficiency of the two beds on each occasion plotted against the rate of revolution of the distributor demonstrates any effect of frequency of dosing, apart from those resulting from film control, since during the short period of the tests the amount of film could be regarded as constant. As shown in *Fig.* 6.8 there was, as expected, over the greater part of the range, between 15 min and 60 min, a reduction in efficiency resulting from decreasing the frequency of dosing. There was, however, evidence that the optimum rate of revolution, for a clean bed, was between 10 and 15 min for a four-armed distributor with staggered jets. At speeds of revolution greater than these, there appeared to be a lowering of efficiency. It is of interest to note that nitrification was only slightly reduced by low frequency dosing. Results quoted by Levine (1940) and Byrom (1957) also showed that the efficiency as measured by the percentage B.O.D. and O. A. removal respectively, was somewhat higher when dosed at 5–7 min and 8 min intervals respectively than at $2\frac{1}{2}$ min.

It does not follow from the results that the optimum speed of rotation was 10–15 min per rev; to control the film at limits which do not adversely effect the efficiency, it may be necessary to revolve the distributor at speeds slower than once every 15 min, the resultant loss in efficiency more than being made good by the gain in efficiency resulting from the prevention of the film accumulation. The results nevertheless do indicate some advantages other than those attributable to film control, at least over the range 1–15 min per rev. Some such possible benefits of low frequency dosing have been discussed by Stanbridge (1956). He suggested that although the time of retention of some of the liquid is less with low frequency dosing this may be more than offset by the longer retention time of the liquid held interstitially between doses. Work reported by the Water Pollution Research Laboratory (1956b) has shown that the mean retention time may be increased by decreasing the frequency of dosing. Below a certain frequency of dosing, however, the retention time is, of course, reduced. As mentioned previously, however, liquid retention time itself may not be so important providing it is sufficiently long to enable the waste to be transferred to the film. The oxidation of the removed waste can proceed during the period between doses.

In attempting to determine the times of contact at different rates of revolution it was observed that within a minute of the passage of the distributor arm over the section of the bed a flush of effluent was discharged from the bottom of the bed (*Fig.* 6.9). The peak concentration of the chloride appeared in the effluent within the

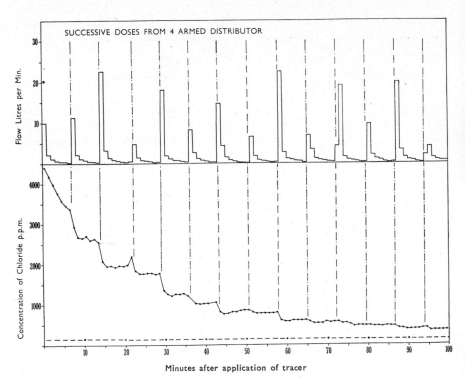

FIG. 6.9. The discharge of chloride from a sector of a bed for 120 min. following one application of chloride to the surface, in relation to the frequency of dosing. (Reproduced from Hawkes, H. A. (1961) An ecological approach to some bacteria bed problems, *J. Inst. Sewage Purif.*, (2) by kind permission of the editor.

first minute but was still being discharged in decreasing amounts three hours later. The reduction in chloride concentration in the effluent took place not at a steady rate but in a series of regularly timed steps; a drop in concentration coincided with the surges of effluent which immediately followed the passage of a distributor arm over the surface. It would appear that when sewage is applied to beds intermittently it passes into the bed as a surge mixing with the interstitial liquid; some of the mixed liquid is displaced in the form of a flush of effluent; the remainder is held interstitially until the next dose, only a small quantity draining away during this period. The amount held interstitially within the bed is, therefore, important in determining the efficiency of a bed intermittently fed, because whilst the liquid was held in the bed, purification would be proceeding. It may well be that such a bed would be more efficient if constructed of medium smaller than the conventional medium used today; the low film concentration associated with the process would make this possible.

Low frequency dosed beds are thus quite different hydraulically and in the course of purification from conventional beds. In the latter the waste is considered to be oxidized as it percolates downward over the medium, this course of oxidation at different depths being expressed mathematically by Velz's equation (page 111). In low frequency dosed beds the course of purification must be considered more in relation to time than depth. Certainly the concept implicit in the terms "percolating" or "trickling" filters is not applicable to low frequency dosed beds, which are better considered as surge filled aerobic contact beds. In view of the rapid mixing of feed and interstitial liquid they are in this respect analogous with the modern complete mixing activated sludge processes.

Danckwerts (1954), comparing the piston and complete mixing types of continuous flows through processing units generally, considered that because of the greater spread of the residence time with complete mixing and assuming the rate of the reaction falls off with the extent of the reaction, complete mixing types of reactor were less efficient than the piston flow type. With autocatalytic reactions (such as biological oxidation), however, it was considered that, because of the different rate-of-reaction curve, the completely mixed reactor may be superior. In applying these views to bacteria beds and activated sludge plants, however, it should be borne in mind that the lag phase is probably absent.

A further advantage of low frequency dosing, it was suggested, is that the higher instantaneous rate of dosage results in a greater volume of the bed medium being wetted and thereby the effective capacity of the bed is increased. To investigate this suggestion, the lateral spread of sewage applied to the surface of a clean bed as jets 12 in. apart was assessed by collecting and measuring the sewage in twelve 2 in. wide adjacent trays placed parallel (tangential) to the travel of the jets so as to collect the liquid from an area 1 ft × 2 ft. Measurements were made immediately above the surface of the bed and at three depths within the bed and at different speeds of revolution of the distributor arm. In each case the results were expressed on a percentage basis and are shown as histograms in *Fig*. 6.10. Most of the lateral spread occurred as the jet impinged on the bed surface; there was, however, no indication that with slower speeds of revolution the lateral spread was greater.

Although other advantageous effects of low frequency dosing may exist, it is considered that the control of excessive film accumulation, with the resultant increased efficiency, is probably the most important effect.

An appreciation of the nutritional method of film control operative in low frequency dosing and the resultant beneficial effects on bed efficiency, makes possible the reasonable application of the principle. No increase in efficiency could be expected of a bed in which film accumulation never occurred, by slowing down the rate of revolution of the distributor to speeds slower than 10 min per rev for example; slower rates of revolution would probably result in decreased efficiency due to decreased retention times. For a similar reason, because film accumulation is usually associated with winter conditions, the frequency of dosing necessary to suppress winter accumulations could be lower than the optimum required for summer conditions. On this basis, variable frequency of dosing is desirable. Whether the extra cost of providing variable speed drives is justifiable will depend upon the degree of deterioration in efficiency during the summer due to the low frequency dosing. At Ewell, for example, Stanbridge (1958) considered that the decrease in efficiency in the summer months which resulted from low frequency dosing was not sufficient to justify changing the speed of rotation, which during the winter gave marked improvements in efficiency.

A bed already ponding cannot be immediately cured by merely slowing down the speed of rotation of the distributor; the periods of low waste concentration between doses, necessary for nutrient control, would not occur under conditions of continuous ponding. If the success of low frequency dosing is due to nutrient control, then it

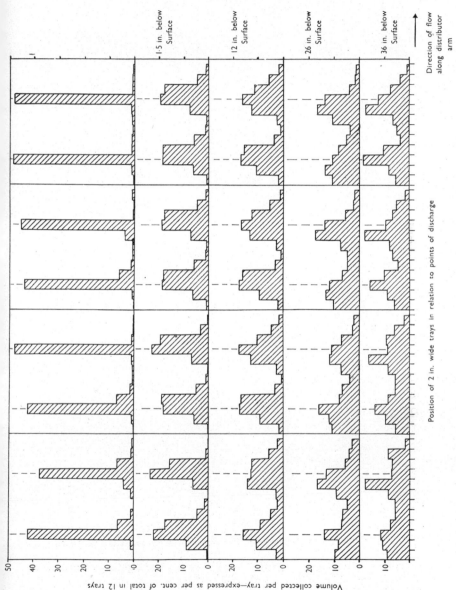

Fig. 6.10. Lateral spread of sewage from 2 jets 12 in. apart at the surface and at three depths within the bed, at four different rates of revolution of the distributor arms. (Reproduced from Hawkes, H.A. (1961) An ecological approach to some bacteria bed problems, *J. Inst. Sewage Purif.* (2) by kind permission of the editor).

can only be effective in controlling a film of living organisms, fungal or bacterial, and not against an accumulation of non-living solids. The possible accumulation of flocculated solids in beds treating wastes with high suspended and colloidal matter during the colder periods when oxidation is retarded, has previously been discussed. The overall effect of low frequency dosing on such beds is not fully known. One could expect that apart from nutritional control of the organisms, the resultant higher instantaneous rate of application would result in a deeper penetration of the flocculation zone to within the bed where temperature would be higher. It is also possible that the higher instantaneous rates of application could flush away some of the flocculated solids even though the living film resists such action. Similarly, if solids applied with the waste or those formed chemically or physically within the beds accumulate, they cannot be controlled by nutritional methods and low frequency dosing could only succeed by virtue of the high instantaneous rates of application as in the case of solids flocculating within the bed.

*Practical Methods of Controlling the Frequency of Dosing*

In determining the frequency of dosing—best expressed as the time in minutes between successive doses—consideration should be given to unit small areas representative of one stone on which the microorganisms live. Thus on a circular bed served by a four armed distributor, the jets of which are not less than 1 ft apart and are staggered on all four arms, the frequency of dosing at the surface is the time of one complete revolution of the distributor. Even at a depth of 1 ft the degree of lateral spread results in the frequency of dosing at this depth, being half the time of revolution of the distributor. It is only within the depths of the bed where the lateral spread of the waste ensures that the flow from one jet is evenly distributed over at least 1 ft that the frequency of dosing can be considered as one quarter of the time of revolution. Troublesome growths usually occur in the upper layers of the bed and in this respect circular beds having distributors with staggered jets are capable of creating conditions of low frequency dosing in the upper layers, to prevent film accumulation and a higher dosing frequency within the bed. Rectangular beds, having the conventional reciprocating distributors, have the same frequency of dosing at all depths. Also, when dosing in both directions, the frequency of dosing differs at different positions along the length of travel. By having distributors with two arms, the jets in which are staggered, and which dose alternately in opposite directions, the conditions of the circular beds could be approached. The jet spacing should be sufficient to ensure that in the upper layers of the bed each unit small area receives waste mostly from one arm only. This can be ensured by having half the width of a bed dosed in one direction and the other half dosed in the opposite direction but the frequency of dosing is then the same at all depths. Low frequency dosing can be applied to conventional single filtration or to supplement the growth controlling effects of recirculation or A.D.F.

The optimum frequency of dosing will depend upon the different operating conditions and the growth promoting properties of the waste. As mentioned previously the optimum frequency may vary seasonally, thus making some variability in dosing frequency desirable. In such two stage processes as A.D.F. it is possible that the optimum frequency of dosing of the primary and secondary stages differs; a lower frequency being necessary to control film growth in the primary stage. The frequent alteration would be made practicable by providing variable frequency of dosing. Generally by providing for a dosing frequency range of 10 to 30 min in the upper layers of the bed, most conditions of operation should be covered.

The conventional reaction-jet propelled distributors on circular beds rotate at rates varying with the flow, but usually faster than 1 rev in 3 min. This rate of rotation can be decreased somewhat by turning some of the jets to discharge in the opposite direction to the driving jets and thus act as a brake. The extent to which this method can be carried is limited by the need to ensure rotation of the distributor at low flows and under windy conditions. Generally it is not possible to satisfactorily reduce the speed of rotation to rates slower than 1 rev in 10 min by this method or by other methods involving a non-differential braking device.

Rotating distributors, propelled by a water-powered wheel travelling around a circumferential track or rail, usually have a slower rate of rotation and are more amenable to some adaptation for lower frequency dosing, by changing the travelling wheel for one of smaller diameter, for example. The application of the water wheel system has been successfully used at Coventry in a braking device which is attached to the conventional reaction-jet distributors (Bennett, discussion Tomlinson and Hall, 1955). To obtain extreme low frequency dosing (1 rev in 20–30 min) the most satisfactory method is probably to provide some form of motor-drive. This could either be attached to the distributor arm and travel round the track as at Ewell (Stanbridge, 1956), or be stationary and drive through geared wheels on the central distributor column. Such systems could readily include provision for variable speed drives.

To ensure the rotation of the distributors and evenness of distribution under conditions of low flows experienced at some works, the distributors are fed through syphon-operated dosing chambers. It has been suggested that these provide some degree of low frequency dosing, but in practice this does not always appear to be effective, probably because for most of the time the period of application is too long in relation to the intervening rest periods.

Most investigations on the effects of frequency of dosing have been carried out on circular beds and difficulties have been experienced in applying the results to rectangular beds with reciprocating distributors. The frequency of dosing is affected both by the speed of travel and the distance of travel. Unlike circular beds where the extent of travel — 360° — is fixed, it is possible to design rectangular beds so that at speeds of travel which can be satisfactorily maintained by the driving power provided, the requisite frequency of dosing is achieved. In fact many of the water-wheel propelled distributors on rectangular beds complete one journey in about 20 min, thus achieving low frequency dosing. With such distribution, however, no provision is available for varying the frequency of dosing and unlike the rotating distributors with staggered jets, they do not provide a higher frequency of dosing within the bed than at the surface. With motor-driven distributors, by using a longer distance of travel, although economy is effected by the use of fewer machines required, each machine must be capable of distributing a greater flow and the higher speed of travel necessary, results in greater wheel wear per machine.

*Application of Low Frequency Dosing to Double Filtration*

According to Howland (1958) the contact time in beds is directly proportional to the depth and inversely proportional to the surface hydraulic loading

$$t \propto \frac{D}{Q^{0.66}}$$

Thus theoretically, in two-stage filtration of whatever form, where, compared with a similarly loaded single bed, both $D$ and $Q$ can be considered as doubled, the resultant time of contact ($t$) is increased. As discussed previously the importance of time of contact, or liquid retention time, probably depends upon the nature of the waste; the removal of colloidal and readily physically adsorbed matter being less affected than that of wastes in true solution.

Probably more important than the increased retention time with two-stage filtration, is the provision of two distinct environments where organisms responsible for carbonaceous oxidation and nitrifying organisms can exist separately. Without becoming involved in the controversy whether nitrification occurs in the presence of organic matter (Fry, 1955), experience with bacteria beds leads one to believe that the autotrophic nitrifying organisms—at least nitrate producing organisms—cannot successfully compete with the more vigorously growing heterotrophic organisms in the presence of available organic nutrient. Thus nitrification is suppressed in the presence of active carbonaceous oxidation, as in the upper layers of a conventional bed where the growth of the heterotrophic bacteria and fungi may produce considerable development of film. The nitrifying organisms are thus restricted to the depths of the bed where the reduced nutrient concentration limits the development of the heterotrophic organisms. Thus nitrification in the presence of organic matter could be restricted, not by the organic matter itself, but by the suppression of the necessary bacterial flora in competition for oxygen and living space with heterotrophic organisms. This view is supported by the fact than in A.D.F. the amount of nitrification is much the same in the primary stage, where the organic concentration of the waste is higher, as in the secondary stage. On this basis it was considered that two-stage filtration without alternation would result in a higher degree of nitrification.

Previous investigations comparing double filtration with other methods of filtration showed that although under favourable conditions double filtration gave good results, the tendency of the primary bed to clog during the winter made it a less satisfactory process that recir-

12

culation or A.D.F. The success of low frequency dosing in controlling film accumulation suggested that film accumulation in the primary bed of a double filtration plant could be prevented by low frequency dosing. This possibility is being investigated and results so far published (Hawkes, 1961) of a period including two winters, show that excessive accumulations of film in the primary bed have been prevented. The 4 hr O.A. and B.O.D. figures for the final effluent were similar to those from similar beds operating on A.D.F at the same overall rate—150 g.y.d. As expected the nitrification was somewhat greater with double filtration, the difference being more marked at higher hydraulic loadings. Comparisons of different methods of filtration by Peach (1957) at Cheltenham and Tidswell (1960) at Burton have also shown the superiority of double filtration in nitrification.

If low frequency dosing of the primary bed results in double filtration being as efficient as A.D.F. it could be that it is preferable since it would then be possible to differentiate in design and operation between the two beds. For example the secondary bed could have smaller medium and be dosed at a higher frequency than the primary bed. It would also be possible to have primary and secondary beds of different sizes to enable primary and secondary stages to be carried out at different dosage rates.

*High Rate Filtration*

This term is usually applied to several methods of filtration in which the liquor is applied to the bed at high average hydraulic loadings— 500 to several thousand g.y.d. In some cases, as in America, this involves the recirculation of the feed to provide a high dilution ratio. As such it is essentially a growth controlling process. The application of a strong undiluted waste at high hydraulic loadings creates different ecological conditions. The result of such a practice will probably depend on the nature of the waste and the type of growth it produces under the operating conditions prevailing. With wastes having a high colloidal or suspended organic content, the rate of flocculation probably exceeds that of oxidation and as a result much of the film is composed of flocculated solids. At the high hydraulic rates, the downward rate of flow could remove such unoxidized solids, the bed then acting as a bioflocculation plant, although according to Heukelekian (1945a) it is still capable of biological oxidation. If the waste supports a bacterial, as opposed to a fungal growth, it is probable that the high hydraulic rates could bring about periodic sloughing of the film as described by Cooke and Hirsch (1958) and Reid and Assenzo (1960). Such sloughing would only occur after considerable accumulation of the film had occurred. When the film is dominated by fungus the resultant tougher growth is able to develop to a greater thickness before being sloughed away by the downward flow of liquid. *Fusarium*, which has tenacious holdfasts, may form the base of such growths on which other organisms become secondarily established. It is when those secondary growths create unfavourable conditions below that the original anchoring growths of *Fusarium* die, and the whole of the film then sloughs off.

In these methods of filtration which rely on the physical scouring of the film, the amount of film present is usually greater than that considered desirable for most satisfactory purification. However, such beds are capable of more than 80 per cent removal of B.O.D. and where a high quality nitrified effluent is not essential, they form a useful economical method of reducing the polluting load of a discharge. They could also be used as pretreatment units before activated sludge plants or bacteria beds.

Although it is not necessary to control film at the low level desirable in conventional beds, the amount present should not impede the free passage of waste or the ventilation of the bed. If ponding results, the downward flow of liquid is impeded and the scouring action reduced. Eventually the film decomposes under the anaerobic conditions so created to form a watery sludge. At such times the efficiency of the bed is greatly reduced and thus the occurrence of such conditions should be prevented. The thickness of film which can be supported without causing such conditions depends upon the size of the voids which is in turn a function of the medium size. Larger voids would also facilitate the passage of the sloughed film through the bed. The solids discharged would probably be composed of larger particles than the humus resulting from the grazing activity of the macrofauna in conventional beds. Investigations on high rate filtration (*Water Pollution Research* 1951) showed that whereas beds constructed of smooth gravel $1\frac{1}{2}$ in. to 3 in. in size did not pond seriously when operated at 600 g.y.d., beds constructed of smaller medium ponded continuously during the winter at different rates ranging from 200–1000 g.y.d.

# CHAPTER 7

# FURTHER ECOLOGICAL CONSIDERATIONS IN THE DESIGN AND OPERATION OF BACTERIA BEDS

EVEN in methods of filtration involving nutritional control of the film, the growth rate $(R_g)$ will be positive and has to be countered by a removal rate $(R_r)$. Unless this is achieved, ponding will eventually result and the efficiency of the growth-limiting processes will be further reduced, bringing about a rapid deterioration in conditions. Also the higher instantaneous rates of application, usually involved in such processes, result in more serious ponding if the process breaks down. In most beds operating at conventional rates, the chief film removal factor is provided by the activity of the grazing fauna. Even high rate beds which normally rely on physical control of film may at times depend upon the activity of grazing fauna for their continued efficiency. In the investigations mentioned above (*Water Pollution Research* 1951) it was found necessary to allow an *Anisopus* and *Psychoda* population to become established before the beds could be successfully operated. The establishment and maintenance of an active grazing fauna is thus essential for the successful operation of bacteria beds. The operational requirements necessary to ensure suitable ecological conditions for such a population are a useful guide to bacteria bed operation.

## Maturation

With many wastes, including domestic sewage, the micro-organisms responsible for their breakdown readily become established in the plant, being introduced with the waste water. With specific organic wastes the establishment of the necessary flora may take some time. In such cases the process of maturation can be speeded by inoculating the bed either from a stored culture of the organisms concerned or from a plant treating the same waste. A satisfactory practical method of inoculating, in the latter case, would be to apply fresh unsettled effluent containing the humus from an appropriate bed, or the effluent from an aeration tank containing activated sludge known to be capable of oxidizing the waste. Since the lag phase of growth of micro-organisms is longer at lower temperatures, an active population of organisms is more rapidly established in the warmer months.

A bacteria bed is often considered matured once nitrification becomes established. Ecologically, however, a bed is only mature when a satisfactory balance between film and grazing fauna has been established. Because micro-organisms are more ubiquitous and more widely dispersed in water and air and because of their rapid rate of multiplication, not only is their chance of being introduced into the bed greater than that of grazing fauna, but their initial rate of colonization is more rapid.

Initially then, there is no effective removal rate $(Rr)$ and until such a force becomes established the growth rate $(R_g)$ of the film should obviously be limited to prevent excessive accumulation of film and ponding. At first little purification of the waste is effected and as a result the concentration of waste at different depths of the bed is much the same and thus the growth rate $(R_g)$ of the film is similar throughout the depth of the bed. As the developing film in the upper part of the bed removes more organic matter, the concentration available to the film in the depths of the bed reduces the growth rate. The extent to which this control of film within the bed is effected depends on the temperature and hydraulic rate of application, the controlling effect being greater at higher temperatures and low rates of application. It is thus essential that at first the load to the bed should be severely restricted and that it should only be increased in stages to match the increasing purification capacity of the developing film. The design flow should not be applied until an active grazing fauna population has become established. It is possible that before such a condition is reached, satisfactory purification, even with nitrification, may be obtained. However, the positive growth rate of the film will eventually bring about a reduction in efficiency unless a grazing population becomes established. Taylor (1960), in reporting his experiences in maturing beds at Bradford, noted that although during the first few months there was a gradual improvement in efficiency, this was usually followed by a marked deterioration for one or two weeks before the beds fully matured.

The time needed for the establishment of the necessary grazing fauna is determined by several factors. Organisms may enter the beds by chance, as eggs introduced by the waste water, or by aerial invasion by adult insects. In the case of beds brought into operation in the vicinity of existing beds, there is every chance of a rapid aerial dispersal to the new beds by flies during periods of suitable climatic conditions. Also beds constructed on the site of land irrigation areas could similarly be inoculated. Although in time most beds would be invaded by macro-fauna, the process can often be speeded up by the intentional introduction of organisms. The introduction of grazing fauna into beds was widely practised some years ago. *Achorutes* were not only despatched all over this country, but were also exported to places as far afield as Stockholm, Chicago, Singapore and Pretoria. They became popularly known as "Bell's Bugs" after the worker who publicized their beneficial activities in bacteria beds (Bell, 1926). The organisms introduced should, of course, be a species suited to the environment imposed by the waste and the operational methods practised. For example with low frequency dosed beds, the introduction of *Lumbricillid* worms would be more suitable than introducing *Achorutes*. Different practical methods are available for effecting their introduction. Where practicable, medium from a suitable bed containing an abundance of different stages of grazing fauna should be carefully transferred into pockets in the surface of the new bed. On a large scale it is more practicable to apply fresh humus sludge from an appropriate bed via the feed.

Although the intentional introduction of fauna may be necessary to speed up maturation, it is more important to maintain conditions to provide a suitable environment in which the desirable organisms can become established. By increasing too rapidly the rates of application before an effective grazing fauna is established, excessive film growth may occur throughout the depth of the bed and the resultant ponding would prevent its successful colonization by the introduced fauna, and its eventual maturation would thus be considerably delayed.

The necessity to severely restrict the loading during the initial stages of maturation can be satisfied in different ways. Probably the most satisfactory way is to operate the beds continuously at very low rates of application. With distributors designed for high flows, such as those on beds operating on double filtration and recirculation systems, it may not be possible to satisfactorily distribute the waste at low flows required. In such cases, beds should be operated at as low flows as possible for part of each day followed by a period of rest. In hot weather this rest period should be during the night when the temperatures are lower, and in cold weather during the day. In maturing beds designed to operate by the nutritional control of film, although initially the film growth can be encouraged by the conventional operation of the beds, the later stages of maturation should be carried out whilst operating on the appropriate system. This would not only limit the rate of film accumulation but ensure the establishment of the species of grazing fauna characteristic of the system.

## Small Scale Experimental Beds

For experimental purposes and to assess the treatability of wastes, small beds usually consisting of cylinders 6 ft in depth and up to 1 ft in diameter, have been widely used. Within a few weeks it is possible to assess the degree to which the waste is removable. So much can also be assessed by the use of rotary tubes (Gloyna *et al.*, 1952). The suitability of bacteria beds as a method of treatment, however, can only be determined after longer periods when the bed has been fully matured and a film-grazing fauna balance has been established. With such beds it is usually necessary to introduce the grazing fauna.

Care should be exercised in assessing the rates at which the waste should be treated on large scale beds. The size of medium in such beds should, ideally, be such that its diameter is not greater than one eighth of that of the bed. Account should also be taken of the temperatures at which the beds are operated in relation to those which may be expected in the large scale beds. A further difficulty is in obtaining an effluent sample representative of the final humus tank effluent on the large scale plant. Although satisfactory small humus tanks can be designed for use with such beds, their performance may not be repeated on the large scale plant. The use of paper-filtered samples ignores the polluting load of an effluent attributable to the suspended solids present. Even for comparative investigations, although paper-filtered samples make comparisons easier, the removal of suspended solids eliminates a variable since the settleability of humus solids produced from beds in different conditions may differ.

*Routine Operation of Beds*

Once a bed has been matured, the essence of efficient operation is the maintenance of the balance of populations. To maintain this ecological balance in populations, continuity of operation is essential. The effect of a period of disuse of a bed depends upon its duration, the original condition of the bed and the climatic conditions prevailing. For some time after the application of the waste to the bed is stopped, the interstitial liquid gradually drains out of the bed for a period depending upon the water-holding capacity of the film. As the surface layers dry out the grazing fauna retreat into the depths of the bed and soon large numbers of grazing organisms will be observed leaving the bed. The last drainings from the bed are accompanied by vast numbers of the motile stages of insects and worms, migrating from the inactive bed. The bed is thus seriously depleted of active grazing fauna and presumably the young worms and larvae which hatch from the remaining eggs find conditions unsuitable for development in the drying bed. The pupal stages give rise to flies which, if climatic conditions are favourable, leave such beds in vast numbers. Under such conditions spiders sometimes dominate the scene and whole beds are covered, and the distributors festooned, with their webs.

If a bed, having suffered this depletion of grazing fauna, is put back to operate at normal rates of application, serious consequences will probably result. Such beds, unlike newly constructed ones, are already well inoculated with the necessary micro-organisms, and the film, although possibly having suffered as a result of the period of inactivity, rapidly recovers when the application of the waste is resumed. In the absence of grazing fauna the film may rapidly accumulate and result in ponding which then delays the establishment of a grazing fauna. Such a series of events can result in a bed having a reduced efficiency for long periods, in some cases for over a year.

If the operation of a bed has to be interrupted, then the period of inactivity should be restricted to the minimum and if practicable the bed should be operated for periods whenever possible, even though this may not be convenient. By operating beds during the nights only, it has been possible to carry out major modification over a period of a week or more, without affecting their conditions or efficiency. Under conditions of extreme temperatures, a period of inactivity of longer than one day may have adverse effects; when the weather is mild and wet, longer periods are permissible. When prolonged periods of inactivity are unavoidable, it is then essential to carefully re-mature the bed in a similar manner to the initial maturation process.

Under favourable conditions, usually in the spring, and when flow circumstances permit, the periodic resting of a bed, for periods not exceeding 24 hours, can have beneficial results on a bed in which film accumulation has occurred. Besides the period of starvation imposed on the film, the grazing activity of the macro-fauna is encouraged by the absence of the physical flow of liquid which normally limits their activity. By such a practice the spring unloading, when this is necessary, can be speeded up.

*Fly Control*

Although ecologically fly populations are best controlled by nutritional control, i.e. by limiting the degree of film accumulation, it may on occasions be necessary to prevent serious nuisance by direct action. Where practicable this may be achieved by flooding the bed and provided that this is of short duration, the film and probably the worm population will not be seriously affected. A more common practice is the application of insecticides. Although these are probably more selective, worms and Collembola not being affected at the concentrations necessary to kill the flies, the bed effluent may be rendered toxic to life in the receiving stream. For this reason only a small portion of the bed area should be treated at any time. It is usually most practicable to apply the insecticide to the bed as an emulsion or water dispersible powder in the sewage feed. Benzene hexachloride (B.H.C.) at the rate of 1·3 lb of the active gamma isomer per acre of bed has proved successful against *Psychoda* and *Anisopus*. (Tomlinson *et al*. 1949) (Jenkins *et al*. 1949). The effectiveness of such treatments is limited by the degree to which the insecticide is evenly distributed to the bed.

Flies which emerge from the beds often congregate in sheltered positions in the vicinity of beds, where they can be attacked by spraying insecticide. This method of attack has least effect on the ecology of the bed and should not, if carefully carried out, result in a toxic effluent. Theoretically the successive applications of insecticides to a fly population in such an isolated habitat might be expected to result in resistant strains being evolved. So far, however, no such case has been substantiated. Even when insecticide treatments have to be resorted to, they should be restricted to a minimum. A knowledge of the habits of the fly enables insecticides to be used only when nuisance is likely to occur. Fluctuations in the aerial density of *Anisopus* above beds, for example, have been shown to be closely related to climatic conditions (Hawkes, 1961a). There is also evidence that, although *Anisopus* may be abundant above the beds throughout the summer, they rarely enter near-by dwellings as they do in the spring, and applications of insecticide are, therefore, not necessary after the end of June. By a continuous succession of insecticide applications it is possible to replace a fly population by one of worms or Collembola which does not give rise to nuisance (Hawkes, 1955a) and which, once the balance of populations has been re-adjusted, is equally efficient in controlling the film. Once the insecticide treatment ceases, however, the original fauna is rapidly re-established and the continuous use of insecticides, needed to maintain the modified fauna, increases the possibility of a toxic effluent. Such a change in the fauna is best maintained by controlling the physical environment, as achieved by low frequency dosing. In this process, not only is the fauna population limited by the nutritional control of its food—the film, but the resultant higher instantaneous rate of application is considered to favour the more prehensile worms. The degree to which this is effective will probably be affected by such factors as the type of distributor jet, jet spacing, type of medium and the hydraulic loading. In the work previously reported, where low frequency dosing resulted in such a marked change in the fauna (*Fig.* 6.5), the beds were operating on A.D.F. and thus the instantaneous rate of application would be double that of a bed operating on single filtration.

*Design Considerations*

Although a plant has to be designed before it is operated, operational requirements should be the basis of design. The operator should not find himself severely restricted in the degree of control by over-rigid design based on arbitrary criteria. For this reason, the brief discussion on the ecological factors which should be considered in design of beds has been left to follow the operational considerations.

*Site*

Because of the adverse effect of low temperatures, beds should be sited in sheltered positions. Enclosed beds should prove advantageous in this respect. Shelter provided by a screen of trees can, however, cause a nuisance at leaf-fall. Temperatures within the bed are largely determined by the temperature of the waste and in this connection the proximity of the plant to the source of waste may be important, reductions in sewage temperatures may occur in long trunk sewers, for example. Because of the possibility of fly nuisance beds should be at some distance from dwellings, etc., especially those to the leeward in relation to the prevailing winds. Hydraulic considerations are paramount in the design of most plants and the choice of site is obviously important in this respect. In some situations careful siting can enable double filtration to be practised without additional pumping.

*Medium*

The function of the medium is to provide the necessary surface on which the active biological film can be supported and at the same time permit the free flow of waste and air to the film. The size, shape and surface nature of the medium are important features determining the degree to which these functions are carried out and hence affect the efficiency of a bed. Theoretically it appears wasteful in plant capacity that, to provide the necessary surface area, more than half the volume of a bed constructed of conventional medium is occupied by inert matter—the medium. In America several attempts have been made to construct suitable media in units of uniform size, e.g. "Aero-blocks" "Raschig rings", and "Straight's blocks" (Bryan and Moeller, 1960).

Goldthorpe (1944) in this country designed the "Huddersfield Tile". The more recent developments of plastics have permitted the prefabrication of corrugated plastic surfaces as bed medium, trade registered as "Dowpac" (Bryan and Moeller, 1960). Although with this medium the surface area per unit volume of bed is no greater than that of stone media, only 6 per cent of the bed volume is occupied by the material. A development of this type of medium to increase the surface area should further increase its efficiency. The extent to which the grazing fauna could become established on such medium is not known and although bacterial film may be removed hydraulically the possibility of clogging by profuse growths of fungus should not be overlooked.

Until a satisfactory and economic alternative is found, the conventional medium will continue to be used in most cases. Since the type of medium used may affect the ultimate efficiency of the plant, careful consideration should be given to its choice. It has been shown (Howland, 1958) that the *liquid* retention time of liquids flowing over spheres varies inversely with the two-thirds power of the diameter of the spheres. Thus, medium size could be expected to affect liquid retention time. More important, however, is the effect of medium size in determining the amount of film which a given volume of bed can support. The optimum size of medium is determined by two opposing factors; the smaller the medium, the greater the surface area, but the more restricted the interstitial spaces in which the film can accumulate and through which the waste and air can flow. The optimum size of medium is thus the smallest on which the maximum degree of film accumulation, resulting from the conditions of operation, can be accommodated without interfering with the ventilation of the bed or the even distribution of the waste. Since the degree of film accumulation depends upon several factors, including the nature of the waste and method of operation, the optimum size of medium is affected by such factors. It is thus unlikely that there can be a single standard medium for all beds, considering the wide range of conditions under which they are operated. Since, at least with conventional beds, the degree of film accumulation is greater in the upper layers, on this basis smaller medium could be used in the depths of the bed. However, the amount of humus in the liquor increases as it passes downward and thus very small medium would be unsuitable. With low frequency dosed beds in which the load is more evenly distributed the size of medium throughout the bed should be the same, providing the lower-most medium is sufficiently large to prevent it passing through the openings in the under-draining. Where the degree of film accumulation can be limited, the use of smaller medium is possible in such beds. The possible use of smaller medium in the secondary bed of double filtration has already been mentioned. The base of the bed should have sufficient slope to prevent the accumulation of humus solids under the tiles which could impede the ventilation of the bed. The presence of "fines" of appreciably smaller size than that considered suitable, even in relatively low proportions by weight, is undesirable. Medium of mixed sizes tends to become consolidated and the interstitial spaces between the suitable medium become restricted by the smaller components. For the same reason the media used should not be susceptible to disintegration and should be handled carefully when filling the beds.

As important as size, is the shape of individual units of medium. Ideally, they should be almost spherical. Excessively long or flat particles tend to pack and restrict the interstitial spaces (Schroepfer, 1951). The nature of the surface of the particles is another factor to be considered. Bacterial slimes and fungal growths can develop on smooth surfaces, such as washed gravel, although the initial lag phase may be somewhat longer. It is probable, however, that a rough surface such as cracked granite, provides a better holdfast for certain grazing fauna. The honeycomb-like structure of slag or clinker is ecologically superior to other standard types of medium. It presents a larger surface area than other media of the same size, even though all of the surface may not be wetted by the waste. Furthermore, it provides an ideal niche for the grazing fauna. One has only to examine a matured piece of slag medium and see the worms, larvae and blue Springtails housed in their ready-made caves and burrows and grazing on the film growing on their doorsteps, to appreciate the hospitable environment it provides.

Economic considerations will undoubtedly be a major factor in the choice of medium. It may be more economical, for example, to use suitable locally available material, even though this may necessitate having slightly larger beds than would be required if a more costly superior form of medium were used. This consideration, however, only applies to the nature of the medium and not to its grading. To use cheap media of indifferent grading containing "fines", or media that will disintegrate to produce "fines" is certainly false economy. Such media will most probably give rise to trouble under extreme operating conditions which could only be remedied at considerable expense and inconvenience.

## Depth

Little consideration has been given to the question of bed depth, and by tradition, most beds in England are approximately 6 ft deep. The depth of the bed, however, is ecologically important in as much as, at a constant loading (G.Y.D), it affects the surface rate of application, and thereby the downward rate of flow of the waste. In conventional beds with high frequency dosing, the increase in surface loading with increase in bed depth could cause excessive accumulations of solids near the surface of deep beds which would reduce their efficiency. With low frequency dosing, however, the more even distribution of the film throughout the depth of the bed should make possible the use of beds considerably deeper than 6 ft. Where this is possible it would reduce the land area required and the size of base and underdraining. The numbers of distributors would be reduced but their capacity would need to be greater. The retaining walls, however, become increasingly more expensive with increase in height above ground level; this being more so with rectangular beds than with circular ones. Where hydraulic requirements demand, it will be necessary to provide pumping capacity together with an adequate standby pump. In two stage filtration or recirculation, where pumping is only required for the primary or returned effluent, it is often possible to continue to apply the waste by gravity to the beds when pump failure occurs. This would not be possible in the case of a deep (high) bed where pumping was normally required. Theoretically on the basis of the formula:

$$t \propto \frac{D}{Q^{0.66}} \text{ (Howland, 1958)}$$

where $D = $ Depth and $Q = $ Surface loading, by increasing the depth and proportionately increasing the surface loading to maintain the same G.Y.D. loading, the liquid retention time is increased.

*Shape*

Although the old method of fixed spray distribution allowed full use to be made of any shape of available area, modern methods of distribution usually determine the bed shape as rectangular or circular. Other shapes demand complication in the design of distributors. Rectangular beds are usually only found on the larger works although some large works have circular ones. Ecological differences occur because of the different distribution methods imposed by the different shapes. The rectangular beds, although more readily ensuring an even distribution of waste across the width of the bed, are not so readily adapted for low frequency dosing, as previously discussed.

*Ventilation*

Although ventilation is essential for the successful operation of beds, the method by which it is effected is not fully understood. It is probable that several forces are at play in effecting ventilation, and the extent to which each contributes varies under varying operating conditions. In most beds, at most times, the temperature differences between the interior of the bed and the air above the bed results in convection currents which effect ventilation. It has been calculated that a difference of 1°F is sufficient to give adequate ventilation to a bed treating sewage at normal rates *(Water Pollution Research,* 1955). The importance of maintaining a thin film so as not to impede the ventilation currents and to ensure that all the organisms in the film receive an adequate supply of oxygen has already been discussed. Structurally, provision should be made for the ventilation of the bed from below. With circular beds having underdrains discharging into a circumferential open channel, these should provide adequate ventilation, providing that they are not surcharged. The use of open stone walling for such beds is probably not essential and it certainly provides an attractive shelter for flies. Where the underdrains discharge into one small common effluent channel within the bed, the provision of ventilation shafts on the periphery of the bed would seem to be a wise measure. With rectangular beds having the underdrains discharging independently to a longitudinal channel to the outside of the bed, or to a channel in a well ventilated duct within the bed, the underdrains should themselves provide adequate ventilation providing that they are kept open. From an aeration point of view beds cannot be over ventilated, although in the winter this could lead to an undesirable reduction in bed temperatures. Since in most beds ventilation is probably not a limiting factor, the provision of forced ventilation has not always proved beneficial. It could possibly increase the efficiency of enclosed beds and those treating strong wastes.

### Distribution of Waste

As we have seen, the method of distributing the waste can markedly affect the ecology of the bed and thereby its efficiency. Distributor design is an integral part of bed design and should be considered in relation to the proposed method of operation. Difficulties arise in providing for even distribution of the waste over a wide daily range of flows experienced at some works. At very low flows recirculation of effluent is recommended. On the whole, if even distribution over the whole flow range is unattainable, the distributor should be designed to ensure even distribution at average flows and above, rather than at very low flows. This being so, the uneven distribution at low flows can be regarded as producing a greater degree of underloading in some places, but the uneven distribution at high flows can only result in a greater over-loading in some places—a much more serious effect. The view that a dribbling jet is likely to produce more growth than a normal jet is based on the erroneous mechanistic concept of film control. Apart from the possibility of freezing in winter, and provided that the distributor is in motion, dribbling during periods of low flow should have no adverse effect. The provision of motor-drives for distributors ensures movement at times of low flow besides providing for controlled frequency dosing and makes unnecessary the provision of syphon dosing chambers.

With normal jets the spacing between them should be such that at average flows the distance between jets lines made by all the distributor arms serving one area of the bed are not greater than 6 in. On circular beds, to ensure even distribution along the radius, some distributors have jets of the same size spaced at increasing distances towards the centre of the bed. Even distribution, however, is probably better achieved by having the jets equally spaced and having a progressive reduction in the diameter of the jets towards the centre of the bed. In beds where nutritional methods of film control are practised, the use of more widely spaced jets with splash plates, to ensure even distributions, should be equally satisfactory. By spraying or cascading the waste from the distributors, the increased aeration should be beneficial but the amount of oxygen so dissolved can only satisfy a fraction of the total oxygen demand.

Fixed spray-jets, because they provide a continuous rain of waste on the surface of beds, encourage excessive growths of film and most have now been replaced by travelling distributors giving a lower frequency of dosing. They could, however, be used on the secondary bed of a double filtration unit, where the low nutrient concentration should not result in excessive growths of film. Such a method of application would probably enhance nitrification within the bed.

Because of the need to ensure continuity of operation, distributors independently driven are superior to those rope-hauled in groups. Even when use is made of the provision for uncoupling a faulty distributor for attention, when this is possible, the area served by it receives no sewage, whereas it is sometimes possible to permit an independently driven distributor to cover the extra area by extending the length of travel.

*Ancillary Plant*

As mentioned previously beds should not be used to remove settleable solids and it is usually necessary to provide adequate settlement of the waste before it is applied to the beds. It is equally important to remove the humus solids discharged from the bed before the effluent passes to the receiving stream. The conventional method is to settle these solids in humus tanks; deep tanks of small cross sectional area which provide a fairly even rate of upward flow are probably the best type. The humus sludge should not be retained for any length of time. If nitrification is occurring in the bed, the denitrification, which would rapidly occur in the anaerobic conditions in the tank, could liberate nitrogen gas which, in rising, would carry the sludge to the surface. The sludge should be removed at least once or twice each day if not continuously. The monthly washing down of humus tanks, where practicable, should also prove beneficial.

13

Humus from beds differs considerably, depending on the waste being treated and the condition of the bed, some having better settling qualities. However efficient the humus tanks, some finely divided solids are, in practice, always present in the effluent and these form a considerable portion of the oxygen demand of many effluents. Their removal can be effected by sand filtration or microstrainers. Where land is available the irrigation of the effluent over a grass plot is a simple and effective method of removing most of the solids and effecting clarification when necessary (Daviss 1957). Such grass plots should be used for the removal of the finely divided solids which do not settle in humus tanks, and not to replace humus tanks or supplement grossly inefficient tanks, unless the frequent removal of the accumulated solids from the plots is anticipated.

# REFERENCES

AGERSBORG, H.P.K. and HATFIELD W. D. (1929). The biology of a sewage treatment plant — A preliminary survey, Decatur, Illinois, *Sewage Wks. J.* **1,** 411—24.

ALLEN, L.A. (1944) The bacteriology of activated sludge, *J. Hyg. Camb.* **43,** 424—31

ALLEN, L.A., TOMLINSON T. G. and NORTON I. L. (1944) The effect of treatment in percolating filters on bacterial counts, *J. Inst. Sew. Purif.,* 115—32.

ARDERN, E. and LOCKETT, W.T. (1936) Laboratory tests for ascertaining the condition of activated sludge, *J. Inst. Sew. Purif.* (1) 212—15, also *City of Manchester Rivers Department Annual Report* 1928, *Appendix* 1, 40—6.

BAINES, S. and FINLAYSON, L.H. (1949) Record of an ichneumon attacking *Spathiophora* (Dipt., Cordyluridae) in sewage filter beds, *Ent. mon. Mag.* **85,** 150—1.

BAINES, S., HAWKES, H.A., HEWITT, C.H. and JENKINS, S.H. (1953) Protozoa as indicators in activated sludge treatment, *Sewage industr. Wastes* **25,** 1023—33.

BALDWIN, E. (1959) *Dynamic Aspects of Bio-chemistry* (3rd ed.), C.U.P.

BARKER, A.N. (1946) The ecology and function of protozoa in sewage purification, *Ann. appl. Biol.* **33,** 314—25.

BARKER, A.N. (1949) Some microbiological aspects of sewage purification, *J. Inst. Sew. Purif.,* (1) 7—22.

BARRACLOUGH D.H. (1954). Biological filtration of sewage and vacuum filtration of sludge—Experimental work at Reading 1949—54, *J. Inst. Sew. Purif.* (4) 361—76.

BARRITT, N. W. (1933) The nitrification process in soils and biological filters, *Ann. appl. Biol.* **20,** 165—84.

BELCHER, E.H. (1951) Experimental studies on the fate of radioactive materials in sewage treatment, *J. Inst. Sew. Purif.* (3) 348—62.

BELL, H.D. (1926) Research on the composition of the grey slimy growth on the surface of sewage filters, *Proc. Ass. Sewage Disp. Wks,* 111—40.

BENNETT, G.W. (1955) Discussion on TOMLINSON and HALL, *J. Inst. Sew. Purif.* (1) 51.

BISSET, K.A. (1950) *The Cytology and Life-History of Bacteria,* Livingstone, Edinburgh, 18.

BISSET, K.A. and MOORE, F.W. (1952) *Bacteria,* Livingstone, Edinburgh,

BLOODGOOD, D.E. (1944) Application of the sludge index test to plant operation, *Water Wks. and Sewerage* **91,** 222.

BROUGHALL, F.G., EVANS, R.B. and GARNETT, P.H. (1960) Investigation and treatment of trade effluents, *J. Inst. Sew. Purif.,* 248—60.

BRYAN, E.H. and MOELLER, D.H. (1960) Aerobic biological oxidation using Dowpac. *Proc. 3rd Biol. Waste Treatment Conf.,* Manhattan; Paper No. 42.

BURNS, R.H. (1959) Disposal of radioactive wastes, *The Effects of Pollution on Living Material,* (Ed. YAPP, W.B.) Institute of Biology, London, 103—12.

BUSCH, A.W. and KALINSKE, A.A. (1956) The utilization of the kinetics of activated sludge in process and equipment design, *Biological Treatment of Sewage and Industrial Wastes* (Ed. MCCABE, J. and ECKENFELDER, W.W.) Reinhold, New York, 277—83.

BUSWELL, A.M. (1931) The biology of activated sludge—An historical review, *Sewage Wks J.* **3,** 362—8.

BUSWELL, A.M. and LONG, H.L. (1923) Microbiology and theory of activated sludge. *J. Amer. Wat. Wks. Ass.* **10,** 309—21.

BUTCHER, R.W. (1932) Contribution to our knowledge of the ecology of sewage fungus. *Trans. Brit. mycol. Soc.* **17,** 112—23.

BUTTERFIELD, C.T. (1935) Studies of sewage purification; II A zöoglea forming bacterium isolated from activated sludge, *Publ. Hlth Rep., Wash.* **50,** 671—84.

BUTTERFIELD, C.T., RUCHHOFT, C.C. and McNAMEE, P.D. (1937) Studies of sewage purification; VI—Biochemical oxidation by sludges developed by the pure culture of bacteria isolated from activated sludge, *Sewage Wks J.* **9,** 173—96.

BUTTERFIELD, C.T. and WATTIE, E. (1941) Studies of sewage purification; XV— Effective bacteria in purification by trickling filters, *Sewage Wks J.,* **13,** 639—58.

BYROM, D. (1957) A short exercise on the periodicity of dosing of laboratory percolating beds, *J. Inst. Sew. Purif.* (2) 155—8.

COOKE, W.B. and HIRSCH, A (1958) Continuous sampling of trickling filter populations (ii) populations, *Sewage industr. Wastes* **30,** 138—56.

COOKE, W.B. and LUDZACK, F. J. (1958) Predacious fungus behaviour in activated sludge systems, *Sewage industr. Wastes* **30,** 1490—5.

CRISP, G. and LLOYD, Ll. (1954) The community of insects in a patch of woodland mud, *Trans. R. ent. Soc., Lond.* **105,** 269—314.

CUTLER, D.W. and BAL, D.V. (1926) The influence of protozoa on the process of nitrogen fixation by *Azotobacter chröococcum, Ann. appl. Biol.* **13,** 516.

DANCKWERTS, P.V. (1954) Continuous flow of materials through processing units, *Industr. Chem. Mnf.* **30,** 102—6.

DAVISS M.R.V. (1951) Alternating double filtration at works of the Birmingham Tame and Rea District Drainage Board, *Sewage industr. Wastes* **23,** 437—50.

DAVISS, M.R.V. (1957) The treatment of humus tank effluent on grass plots at the works of the Birmingham Tame and Rea District Drainage Board, *Surveyor* **116,** 613—4.

DAWSON, P.S.S. and JENKINS, S.H. (1949) The oxygen requirements of activated sludge determined by manometric methods, *Sewage Wks. J.* **21,** 643—58.

DICKINSON, D. (1960) The origin, treatment and disposal of effluents in the food canning and freezing industries, *Waste Treatment* (Ed. ISAAC, P.C.G.), Pergamon Press, Oxford, 391—4.

DUNBAR, DR. and CALVERT, H.T. (1908) *Principles of Sewage Treatment,* Griffin (London), 23.

DYSON, J.E.B. and LLOYD, Ll. (1933) Remarks on the flies breeding in the bacteria beds at the Knostrop Sewage Works, Leeds, *J. Inst. Sew. Purif.* (2) 28—33.

EDWARDS, G.P. (1949) Factors affecting the efficiency of activated sludge plants— a discussion, *Sewage Wks. J.* **21.** 640—2.

ELTON, C.S. (1927) *Aminal Ecology,* Sidgwick and Jackson, London.

ELTON, C.S. (1935) *Animal Ecology,* Sidgwick and Jackson, London.

ENGELBRECHT, R.S. and McKINNEY, R.E. (1957) Activated sludge cultures developed on pure organic compounds, *Sewage industr. Wastes* **29,** 1350—62.

FOWLER, G.J. (1907) in DIBDIN, W.J., The disposition and analysis of sewage debris in contact beds, *Analyst* **32,** 108—16.

FRANKLAND, E. (1870) *Rivers Pollution Commission* 1868, Ist report, 1,70.

FRY, B.A. (1955) *The Nitrogen Metabolism of Micro-organisms,* Methuen, London.

GADEN, E.L. (1956) Aeration and oxygen transport in biological systems—basic considerations, *Biological Treatment of Sewage and Industrial wastes* (Ed. McCabe, J. and Eckenfelder, W.W.) Reinhold, New York, 172—91.

Gameson, A.L.H. and Wheatland, A.B. (1958) The ultimate oxygen demand and course of oxidation of sewage effluents, *J. Inst. Sew. Purif.* (2) 106—19.

Gehm, H. W. (1956) Activated sludge at high temperatures and high pH values, *Biological Treatment of Sewage and Industrial Wastes* (Ed. McCabe, J. and Eckenfelder, W. W.), Reinhold, New York, 352—5.

Gellman, I. and Heukelekian, H. (1953) Studies of the biochemical oxidation by direct methods; III—Oxidation and purification of industrial wastes by activated sludge, *Sewage industr. Wastes* **25,** 1196—209.

Gloyna E.F., Comstock, R.F. and Renn, C.E. (1952) Rotary tubes as experimental filters, *Sewage industr. Wastes* **24,** 1355—7.

Goldthorpe H.H. (1944) The "Huddersfield" aeration duct for sewage works percolating beds, *J. Inst. Sew. Purif.* 97—102.

Gould R.H. (1953) Sewage disposal problems in the world's largest city, *Sewage industr. Wastes* **25,** 155—60.

Gould R.H. (1960) Realistic application of the theoretical aspects of aeration processes, *Proc. 3rd Biol. Waste Treatment Conf. Manhattan*; Paper No. 36.

Gray, E. (1952) The ecology of the ciliate fauna in Hobson's Brook, a Cambridgeshire chalk stream, *J. gen. Microbiol* **6,** 108—22.

Greene, G. (1957) Experimental work on the treatment of the British Celanese Ltd. trade waste, *J. Inst. Sew. Purif.* (1) 116—22.

Happold F.C. and Key A. (1932) The bacterial purification of gas works liquors—The action of the liquors on the bacterial flora of sewage, *J. Inst. Sew. Purif.* (2), 252—7.

Hardin, G. (1943) Flocculation of bacteria by protozoa, *Nature, Lond.* **151,** 642.

Harrison, M. E. and Heukelekian, H. (1958) Slime infestation—literature review, *Sewage industr. Wastes* **30,** 1278—1302.

Harrison W. H. (1908) *Royal Commission on Sewage Disposal, 5th report, Appendix 1, Minutes of evidence*, minutes 22037, 22311—14.

Haseltine, T.R. (1956) A rational approach to the design of activated sludge plants, *Biological Treatment of Sewage and Industrial Wastes* (Ed. McCabe, J. and Eckenfelder, W.W.) Reinhold, New York, 257—70.

Hawkes, H.A. (1952) The ecology of *Anisopus fenestralis* (Scop.) (Diptera) in sewage bacteria beds, *Ann. appl. Biol.* **39,** 181—92.

Hawkes H.A. (1954) Some effects of feeding sucrose to the imago of *Anisopus fenestralis* (Scop). and some changes in the habits of the fly on invading the bacteria bed habitat, *Proc. Bgham nat. Hist. Soc.* **18** (4), 55—60.

Hawkes H.A. (1955) The effect of periodicity of dosing on the amount of film and numbers of insects and worms in the alternating double filters at Minworth, Birmingham, *J. Inst. Sew. Purif.* (1) 48—50.

Hawkes, H.A. (1955a) The effects of insecticide treatment on the macrofauna populations, film accumulation and efficiency of sewage percolating filters, *Ann. appl. Biol.* **43,** 122—33.

Hawkes, H.A. (1957) Film accumulation and grazing activity in the sewage filters at Birmingham. *J. Inst. Sew. Purif.* (2) 88—112.

Hawkes, H.A. (1959) The effects of methods of sewage application on the ecology of bacteria beds, *Ann. appl. Biol.* **47,** 339—49.

Hawkes, H.A. (1961) An ecological approach to some bacteria bed problems, *J. Inst. Sew. Purif.* (2) 105—32.

HAWKES, H.A. (1961a) Fluctuations in the aerial density of *Anisopus fenestralis* (Scop.) (Diptera) above sewage bacteria beds, *Ann. appl. Biol.* (49) 66—76.

HAWKES, H.A. and JENKINS, S.H. (1951) Biological principles in sewage purification. *J Inst. Sew. Purif.* (3) 300—17.

HAWKES, H.A. and JENKINS, S. H.(1955) Comparison of four grades of sewage percolating filter media in relation to purification, film accumulation and fauna, *J. Inst. Sew. Purif.* (4) 352—8.

HAWKES, H.A. and JENKINS, S.H. (1958) Comparison of four grades of media in relation to purification, film accumulation and fauna in sewage percolating filters operating on alternate double filtration, *J. Inst. Sew. Purif.* (2) 221—5.

HELMERS, E.N., FRAME, J.D., GREENBURG, A. E., and SAWYER, C.N. (1952) Nutritional requirements in the biological stabilization of industrial wastes; III—Treatment with supplementary nutrients, *Sewage industr. Wastes* **24,** 496—507.

HEUKELEKIAN, H. (1941) Activated sludge bulking, *Sewage Wks.* J. **13,** 39—42.

HEUKELEKIAN, H. (1945) The relationship between accumulation, biochemical and biological characteristics of film, and purification capacity of a biofilter and a standard filter; 1. Film accumulation, *Sewage Wks.* J. **17,** 23—38.

HEUKELEKIAN, H. (1945a) The relationship between accumulation, biochemical and biological characteristics of the film, and purification capacity of a biofilter and a standard filter, *Sewage Wks.* J. **17,** 743—69.

HEUKELEKIAN, H. (1949) Aeration of soluble organic wastes with non-flocculent growths, *Industr. Engng. Chem. (Industr.)* **41,** 1412—15.

HEUKELEKIAN, H. and LITTMAN, M.L. (1939) Carbon and nitrogen transformations in the purification of sewage by the activated sludge process; II—Morphological and biochemical studies of zöogleal organisms, *Sewage Wks.* J. **11,** 752—63.

HEUKELEKIAN, H. and SCHULHOFF, H.B. (1938) Studies on the clarification stage of the activated sludge process; IV—Preliminary notes on the clarifying organisms in activated sludge, *Sewage Wks.* J. **10,** 43—8.

HEY, D. (1955) A preliminary report on the culture of fish in the final effluent from the new disposal works, Athlone, S. Africa, *Verh. int. Ver. Limnol.* **12,** 737—42.

HICKS, R. (1954) *Treatment of Auckland Meat Wastes*, Auckland Metropolitan Drainage Board.

HOLTJE, R.H. (1943) The biology of sewage sprinkling filters, *Sewage Wks.* J. **15,** 14—29.

HOOVER, S.R., JASEWICZ, L., PEPINSKY, J.B. and PORGES, N. (1952) Activated sludge as a source of vitamin $B_{12}$ for animal feeds, *Sewage Industr. Wastes* **24,** 38—44.

HORASAWA, I. (1949) Biological studies on activated sludge in the purification of sewage; II—Characteristics of activated sludge biota and its ecological classification, *J. Water Works and Sewerage Assoc.* (Japan), No. 181,8.

HOWARD, A. (Sir) (1946) Activated and digested sewage sludges in agriculture and horticulture, *J. Inst. Sew. Purif.* (2) 42—3.

HOWLAND, W.E. (1958) Flow over porous media as in a trickling filter, *Proc. 12th. Ind. Waste Conf. Purdue Univ.* 435—65.

HYNES, H.B.N., (1960) *The Biology of Polluted Waters*, U.P. Liverpool.

INGOLD, R.S. (1940) Oxidation-reduction enzymes in activated sludge, *Sewage Wks.* J. 12, 862—74.

INGRAM, W.M., COOKE, W.B. and HAGERTY, L.T. (1958) Snails associated with sewage treatment installations, *Sewage industr. Wastes* **30,** 821—4.

ISAAC, P.C.G. and LODGE, M. (1960) The use of algae for sewage treatment in oxidation ponds, *J. Inst. Sew. Purif.* (4) 376—93.

JACKSON, C.J. (1960) The treatment of distillery and antibiotics wastes, *Waste Treatment* (Ed. ISAAC P.C.G.), Pergamon Press, Oxford, 227.

JENKINS, D. (1960) The use of manometric methods in the study of sewage and trade wastes, *Waste Treatment* (Ed. ISAAC P.C.G.), Pergamon Press, Oxford, 99—125.

JENKINS, S.H. (1942) The role of protozoa in the activated sludge process, *Nature, Lond.* **150**, 607.

JENKINS, S.H., BAINES, S., and HAWKES, H.A. (1949) The control of *Anisopus fenestralis* and factors influencing the numbers of *Anisopus* caught in surface traps, *J. Inst. Sew. Purif.* (2) 178—87.

JENKINS, S.H. and LOCKETT, W.T., (1943) Loss of phosphorus during sewage purification, *Nature, Lond.* **151**, 306—7.

JENKINS, S.H. and WILKINSON, R. (1940) The oxidation of lactose by activated sludge, *J. Soc. chem. Ind. Lond.* **61**, 125—8.

JOHNSON, J.W.H., (1914) A contribution to the biology of sewage disposal, *J. econ. Biol.* **9**, 105—24; 127—64.

KATZ, J.W., and ROHLICH, G.A. (1956) A study of the equilibria and kinetics of adsorption by activated sludge, *Biological Treatment of Sewage and Industrial Wastes* (Ed. McCABE, J., and ECKENFELDER, W.W.) Reinhold, New York, 66—87.

KEEFER, C.E., and MEISEL, J.T. (1953) Activated sludge studies; IV—Sludge age and its effect on the activated sludge process, *Sewage industr. Wastes* **25**, 898—908.

KLEIN, L. (1957) *Aspects of River Pollution* Ch. VIII—Biological aspects of river pollution, HAWKES, H.A., Butterworths, London.

KOLKWITZ, R. (1926) The biology of activated sludge, *Kleine Mitt. Ver. Wasserversorg* **3**, 70—4.

KOLKWITZ, R. (1950) *Oekologie der Saprobien. (Ecology of saprobes—The relation of aquatic organisms to their environment)*, SchrReihe Ver. Wasserhyg, No. 4 Piscator-Verlag, Stuttgart.

KRAUS, L.S. (1945) The use of digested sludge and digester overflow to control bulking activated sludge, *Sewage Wks. J.* **17**, 1177—90.

LACKEY, J.B. (1925) Sprinkling filter bed studies, *Bull. N.J. agric. Exp. Sta.* **427**, 41.

LACKEY, J.B. and WATTIE, E. (1940) Studies of sewage purification; XIII—The biology of *Sphaerotilus natans* (Kutzing) in relation to bulking of activated sludge, *Sewage Wks. J.* **12**, 669.

LEES, H. (1955) *Biochemistry of Autotrophic Bacteria*, Butterworths, London, 8.

LEVINE, M. (1940) The role of trickling filters in sewage purification, *Sewage Wks. J.* **12**, 1062.

LIEBMANN, H. (1949) The biology of percolating filtert, *Vom Wasser*, 17 62—82.

LITTMAN, M.L. (1940) Carbon and nitrogen transformations in the purification of sewage by the activated sludge process (iv) with a culture of *Sphaerotilus*. *Sewage Wks. J.* **12**, 685—93.

LLOYD, LL. (1941) The seasonal rhythm of a fly *Spaniotoma minima* and some theoretical considerations, *Trans. R. Soc. trop. Med. Hyg.* **35**, 93—104.

LLOYD, LL. (1943) Materials for a study in animal competition; Part III—The seasonal rhythm of *Psychoda alternata* Say, and an effect of intraspecific competition, *Ann. appl. Biol.* **30**, 358—64.

LLOYD, LL. (1944) The sewage bacteria bed fauna in its natural setting. *Nature, Lond.* **154**, 397.

LLOYD, LL. (1945) Animal life in sewage purification processes, *J. Inst. Sew. Purif.* (2), 119—39.

LOCKETT, W.T. (1932) Louis Pasteur, his life and work, *Proc. Ass. Sewage Disp. Wks*, 191—200.

LOCKETT, W.T. and GRIFFITHS, J. (1947) Cyanides in trade effluents and their effect on the bacterial purification of sewage, *J. Inst. Sew. Purif.* (2), 121—140.

LOGAN, R.P., and BUDD, W.E. (1956) Effect of B.O.D. loadings on activated sludge plant operation, *Biological Treatment of Sewage and Industrial Wastes*, (Ed. McCABE, J. and ECKENFELDER, W.W.) Reinhold, New York, 271—6.

LUMB, C. (1956) A modified recirculation system, *J. Inst. Sew. Purif.* (4). 383—96.

LUMB, C., and BARNES, J.P. (1948) The periodicity of dosing percolating filters, *J. Inst. Sew. Purif.* (1), 83—98.

LUMB, C. and EASTWOOD, P.K. (1958) The recirculation principle in filtration of settled sewage—some notes and comments on its application, *J. Inst. Sew. Purif.* (4), 380—98.

MACFADYEN, A. (1957) *Animal Ecology, Aims and Methods*, Pitman (London).

McCABE, J. and ECKENFELDER, W.W. (1956) *Biological Treatment of Sewage and Industrial Wastes, Pt. 2. Aeration—theory and design*, Reinhold, New York.

McGAUHEY, P.H. (1960) Reclamation of water from domestic and industrial wastes, *Waste Treatment* (Ed. ISAAC, P.C.G. Pergamon Press, Oxford, 440.

McKINNEY, R.E. (1956) Biological flocculation, *Biological Treatment of Sewage and Industrial Wastes* (Ed. McCABE, J. and ECKENFELDER, W.W.) Reinhold, New York, 88—100.

McKINNEY, R.E. (1957) Activity of micro-organisms in organic waste disposal (ii) aerobic processes, *Appl. Microbiol., Baltimore* **5**, 166—87.

McKINNEY, R.E. and GRAM, A. (1956) Protozoa and activated sludge, *Sewage industr. Wastes* **28**, 1219—31.

McKINNEY, R.E. and HORWOOD, M.P. (1952) Fundamental approach to the activated sludge process; I—Floc-producing bacteria, *Sewage industr. Wastes* **24**, 117—23.

MCNICHOLAS, J. and TENCH, H.B. (1959) A review of recent activated sludge research at Manchester, *J. Inst. Sew. Purif.* 425—35.

MEIKLEJOHN, J. (1932) The effect of *Colpidium* on ammonia production by soil bacteria. *Ann. appl. Biol.* **19**, 584.

MILLS, E.V. (1945) The treatment of settled sewage in percolating filters in series with periodic change in the order of the filters—Results of operation of the experimental plant at Minworth, Birmingham, 1940—1944, *J. Inst. Sew. Purif* (1), 35—49.

MONOD, J. (1949) The growth of bacterial cultures, *Ann. Rev. Microbiol.* **3**, 371—94.

Natural Resources (Technical) Committee (1954), Report, The use of town wastes in agriculture—H.M. Stationery Office, London.

OKUN, D.A. and LYNN, W.R. (1956) Preliminary investigations into the effect of oxygen tension on biological sewage treatment, *Biological Treatment of Sewage and Industrial Wastes*, (Ed. McCABE, J. and ECKENFELDER, W.W.) Reinhold, New York, 192—207.

OLIVER, F. discussion HAWKES, H.A. (1957) *J. Inst. Sewage Purif.* (2), 108.

ORFORD, H.E. (1951) Breaking in a plant for treating gum wastes, *Sewage industr. Wastes.* **23**, 313—8.

ORFORD, H.E., HEUKELEKIAN, H. and ISENBERG, E. (1960) Effect of sludge loading and dissolved oxygen on the performance of the activated sludge process, *Proc. 3rd Biol. Waste Treatment Conf. Manhattan;* Paper No. 30.

O'SHAUGHNESSY, F.R. (1931) Some considerations in the oxidation of sewage, *Proc. Ass. Sewage Disp. Wks.* (1), 74—92.

OVERGAARD, C. (Neilsen) (1949) Studies on the soil microfauna, II—The soil-inhabiting nematodes, *Nat. Jutland.* **2**, 95—119.

OVERGAARD, C. (1949a) Free–living nematodes and soil microbiology, *Proc. 4th Int. Congr. Microbiol., Copenhagen*, 1947, 483—4.

PAINTER, H.A. (1954) Factors affecting the growth of some fungi associated with sewage purification, *J. gen. Microbiol.* **10**, 177—90.

PANKHURST, E.S. (1959) The biological oxidation of spent gas liquor, *J. appl. Bact.* **22**, 202—15.

PARKINSON, W.H. and BELL, H.D., (1919) *Insect Life in Sewage Filters*, Sanitary Publishing Co. London.

PASVEER, A. (1956) Oxygen supply as the limiting factor in activated sludge purification, *Biological Treatment of Sewage and Industrial Wastes* (Ed. McCABE, J. and ECKENFELDER, W.W.) Reinhold, New York, 208—11.

PASVEER, A. (1959) A contribution to the development in activated sludge treatment *J. Inst. Sew. Purif.* (4), 436—65.

PEACH, J.D. (1957) Some percolating filter experiments at Cheltenham, *J. Inst. Sew. Purif.* (2), 11—15.

PETTET, A.E.J. and MILLS, E.V. (1954) Biological treatment of cyanides with and without sewage, *J. Appl. Chem., Lond.* **4**, 434—44.

PETTET, A.E.J. and THOMAS, H.N. (1948) The effect of cyanides on treatment of sewage in percolating filters, *J. Inst. Sew. Purif.* (2), 61—68.

PETTET, A.E.J., TOMLINSON, T.G. and HEMENS, J. (1959) The treatment of strong organic wastes by anaerobic digestion, *J. Inst. publ. Hlth. Engrs.* 58, 170.

PETRU, ING. A. (1958) Temperature and air flow in filters, significance in trickling filter efficiency, *Contract. Rec.* **69**, 15—21.

PICKERING, E.T. (1958) Clean air and clean water—and the gas industry, *Trans. Inst. Gas Engrs,, Lond.* **296**, 527—37.

PILLAI, S.C. and SUBRAHMANYAN, V. (1942) The role of protozoa in the activated sludge process, *Nature, Lond.* **150**, 525.

PILLAI, S.C. and SUBRAHMANYAN, V. (1942—3) Relation of protozoa to bulking of activated sludge, *Sci. and Cult.* **8**, 376—8.

PILLAI, S.C. and SUBRAHMANYAN, V. (1944) The role of protozoa in aerobic purification of sewage, *Nature, Lond.* **154**, 179—80.

PORGES, N., JASEWICZ, L., and HOOVER, S.R. (1956) Principles of biological oxidation, *Biological Treatment of Sewage and Industrial Wastes* (Ed. McCABE, J. and ECKENFELDER, W.W.) Reinhold, New York, 35—48.

PRINGSHEIM, E.G. (1949) The filamentous bacteria *Sphaerotilus, Leptothrix, Cladothrix* and their relation to iron and manganese, *Phil. Trans., R. Soc.,* B. **233**, 453—82.

*Recommended Methods for Analysis of Trade Effluents*, (1958) Soc. for Anal. Chem.Heffer, 18.

REID, G.W. and ASSENZO, J.R. (1960) Biological slimes, *3rd Biol. Waste Treatment Conf. Manhattan*, Paper No. 43.

RENN, C.E. (1956). Biophysical processes in slime, film and floc formation, *Biological Treatment of Sewage and Industrial Wastes* (Ed. McCABE, J. and ECKENFELDER, W.W.) Reinhold, New York, 116—20.

REYNOLDSON, T.B. (1939) The role of macro-organisms in bacteria beds, *J. Inst. Sew. Purif.* (1), 158—72.

REYNOLDSON, T.B. (1941) The biology of the macrofauna of a high rate double filtration plant at Huddersfield, *J. Inst. Sew. Purif.* (1), 109—29.

REYNOLDSON, T.B. (1942) Further studies on the biology of a double filtration plant at Huddersfield, *J. Inst. Sew. Purif.* (1), 116—40.

REYNOLDSON, T.B. (1942a) *Vorticella* as an indicator organism in activated sludge, *Nature, Lond.* **149**, 608.

REYNOLDSON, T.B. (1948) An ecological study of the enchytraeid worm population of sewage bacteria beds—synthesis of field and laboratory data, *J. Anim. Ecol.* **17**, 27—38.

RICHARDS, E.H. and SAWYER, G.C. (1922) Further experiments with activated sludge, *J. Soc. chem. Ind., Lond.* **41**, 62.

RIDENOUR, G.M. (1935) Activated sludge treatment with extremely low solids, *Sewage Wks, J.* **7**, 25—35.

ROSS, W.K. and SHEPPARD, A.A. (1956) Biological oxidation of petroleum phenolic waste waters, *Biological Treatment of Sewage and Industrial Westes* (Ed. McCABE, J. and ECKENFELDER, W.W.) Reinhold, New York, 373.

*Royal Commission on Sewage Disposal (1908) 5th Rep. Appendix*, 1. *Minutes of evidence*, Minutes, 22350—51. Also *Interim Report Vol.* 1., Minutes 7021—3, 7453—4.

RUCHHOFT, C.C., KACHMAR, J.F. and MOORE, W.A. (1940) Studies of sewage purification; XI—The removal of glucose from substrates by activated sludge, *Publ. Hlth. Rep., Wash.* 55, 393—423. Reprint No 2142.

RUCHHOFT, C.C., KACHMAR, J.F. and PLACAK, O.R. (1940a) Studies of sewage purification; XII—Metabolism of glucose by activated sludge, *Publ. Hlth. Rep., Wash.* 55, 582—601. Reprint No. 2149.

RUCHHOFT, C.C. and KACHMAR, J.F. (1941) Studies of sewage purification; XIV—The role of *Sphaerotilus natans* in activated sludge bulking, *Sewage Wks. J.* **13**, 3—32.

RUCHHOFT. C.C. and WATKINS, J.H. (1928) Bacteriological isolation and study of the filamentous organisms in the activated sludge of the Des Plains River Sewage Treatment Plant, *Sewage Wks. J.* **1**. 52—8.

RUSSEL, R. and BARTOW, E, (1916) Bacteriological study of sewage purification by aeration, *Univ. Ill. Bull. State. Water Suvey Series*, No. 13, 348.

SAWYER, C.N. (1956) Bacterial nutrition and synthesis, *Biological Treatment of Sewage and Industrial Wastes* (Ed. McCABE, J. and ECKENFELDER, W.W.) Reinhold, New York, 12.

SCHROEPFER, G.J. (1951) Effect of particle shape on porosity and surface area of trickling filter media, *Sewage industr. Wastes* **23**, 1356—66.

SILVERMAN, P.H. and GRIFFITHS, R.B. (1955) A review of methods of sewage disposal in Great Britain, with special reference to the epizöotiology of *Cysticercus bovis*, *Ann. trop. Med. Parasit.* **49**, 436—50.

SMIT, J. (1934) Bulking of activated sludge (II) on the causative organisms, *Sewage Wks. J.* **6**, 1041—53.

SOLOMON, M.E. (1957) Dynamics of insect populations, *Ann. Rev. Entomol.* **2**, 121—42.

SOUTHGATE, B.A. (1948) *Treatment and Disposal of Industrial Wastes*, H.M. Stationery Office, London, 238.

STANBRIDGE, H.H. (1954) The development of biological filtration, *Wat. Sanit. Engr.* 4, 297—300, 353—8.

STANBRIDGE, H.H. (1956) Thoughts on biological filtration, *J. Inst. Sew. Purif.* (3), 270—89.

STANBRIDGE, H.H. (1958) Experiments at Ewell sewage works to determine the effect of low frequency dosing on filter performance, *J. Inst. Sew. Purif.* (2), 226—7.

STEFFEN, A.J. (1958) Treatment of packing house wastes by anaerobic digestion, *Biological Treatment of Sewage and Industrial Wastes, Vol II* (Ed. McCABE, J. and ECKENFELDER, W.W.), Reinhold, New York, 126—35.

STONE, T. (1955) The fate of chromium during the treatment of sewage, *J. Inst. Sew. Purif.* (4), 345—7.

Stone, T. (1956) The fate of iron and phosphates during the treatment of sewage, *J. Inst. Sew. Purif.* (4), 405—7.

Stone, T. (1958) The fate of copper during the treatment of sewage *J. Inst. Sew. Purif.* (1), 82—3.

Stone, T. (1959) The fate of nickel during the treatment of sewage *J. Inst. Sew. Purif.* (2), 252—4.

Stone, T. (1959) The fate of zinc during the treatment of sewage. *J. Inst. Sew. Purif.* (2), 254—7.

Sugden, B. and Lloyd, Ll. (1950) The clearing of turbid water by means of the ciliate *Carchesium*—A demonstration, *J. Inst Sew. Purif.* (1), 16—26.

Taylor, C.B. (1942) Bacteriology of fresh water; III—Types of bacteria present in lakes and streams and their relationship to the bacterial flora of soil, *J. Hyg., Camb.* **42**, 284.

Taylor, G. (1957) Discussion on Hawkes, (1957) *J. Inst. Sew. Purif.* 2, 108.

Taylor, G. (1960) Maturing of percolating-filters, A symposium, *J. Inst. Sew. Purif.* (4), 370—2.

Taylor, H. (1930) Some biological notes on sewage disposal processes, *Proc. Ass. Sewage Disp. Wks*, 108—19.

Taylor, T.H.C. (1955) Biological control of insect pests, *Ann. appl. Biol.* 43, 190—6.

Terry, R.J. (1951) The behaviour and distribution of the larger worms in trickling filters, *J. Inst. Sew. Purif.* (1), 16—23.

Tidswell, M.A. (1960) Experimental purification of sewage containing a large proportion of brewery wastes at Burton-on-Trent, *J. Inst. Sew. Purif.* (2), 139—54.

Tomlinson, T.G. (1941) The treatment of settled sewage in percolating filters in series with periodic changes in the order of the filters, *J. Inst. Sew. Purif.* (1), 39—57.

Tomlinson, T.G. (1942) Some aspects of microbiology in the treatment of sewage, *J. Soc. chem. Ind. Lond.* **61**, 53—8.

Tomlinson, T.G. (1946) Growth and distribution of film in percolating filters treating sewage by single and alternate double filtration, *J. Inst. Sew. Purif.* (1), 168—78.

Tomlinson, T.G., Grindley, J., Collett, R., and Muirden, M.J., (1949) Control of flies breeding in percolating sewage filters, (Pt. 2), *J. Inst. Sew. Purif.* (2), 127—39.

Tomlinson, T.G. and Hall, H. (1955) The effect of periodicity of dosing on the efficiency of percolating filters, *J. Inst. Sew. Purif.* (1), 40—7.

Tomlinson, T.G. and Stride, G.O. (1945) Investigations into the fly populations of percolating filters, *J. Inst. Sew. Purif.* (2), 140—8.

Torpey, W.N. and Chasick, A.H. (1956) Principles of activated sludge operation, *Biological Treatment of Sewage and Industrial Wastes* (Ed. McCabe, J. and Eckenfelder, W.W.) Reinhold, New York, 284—303.

Underkofler, L.A. and Hickey, R.J., (1954) *Industrial Fermentations Vol. II*, Ch. 14, Buswell, A.M., Chem. Pub. Co., New York.

Usinger, R.L. and Kellen, W.R. (1955) Role of insects on sewage disposal beds, *Hillgardia*, **23**, 263—321.

Velz, C.J. (1948) A basic law for the performance of biological filters, *Sewage Wks. J.* **20**, 607—17.

Viehl, K. and Meissner, B. (1934) Influence of temperature and the time of year on biological treatment of sewage, *Zbl. Bakt.* **91**, 14.

Ware, G.C. (1958) Effect of temperature on the biological destruction of cyanide, *Wat. Sanit. Engr.* **6**, 537.

Ware, G.C. and Painter, H. A. (1955) Bacterial utilization of cyanide, *Nature, Lond.* **175**, 900.

*Water Pollution Research* 1951, H.M. Stationery Office, London, (1952), 13.

*Water Pollution Research* 1955, H. M. Stationery Office, London, (1956), 55—7.

*Water Pollution Research* 1955a, H.M. Stationery Office, London, (1956), 51—2.

*Water Pollution Research* 1956, H.M. Stationery Office, London, (1957), 67—70.

*Water Pollution Research* 1956a, H.M. Stationery Office, London, (1957) 53—4.

*Water Pollution Research* 1956b, H.M. Stationery Office, London, (1957), 42.

*Water Pollution Research* 1957, H.M. Stationery Office, London, (1958), 63—5.

*Water Pollution Technical Paper—No. 8* (1941) The treatment and disposal of waste waters from dairies and milk-product factories, H.M. Stationery Office, London.

WATTIE, E. (1943) Cultural characteristics of zöoglea–forming bacteria isolated from activated sludge and trickling filters, *Sewage Wks. J.* **15**, 476—90.

WATSON, J.M (1943) Anabiosis in a soil ciliate, *Nature, Lond.* **152**, 693—4.

WILSON, I.S. (1954) The Monsanto Plant for the treatment of chemical wastes, *J. Inst. Sew. Purif.* (2), 86—114.

WILSON, I.S. (1959) Discussion on GAMESON, A.L.H. and WHEATLAND, A.B. (1958), *J. Inst. Sew. Purif.* (2), 182.

WILSON, I.S., (1960) Discussion on BROUGHALL, F.G., EVANS R.B., and GARNETT, P.H. *J. Inst. Sew. Purif.* (3), 257.

WILSON, I.S. (1960a) The treatment of chemical wastes, *Waste Treatment* (Ed. ISSAC, P.C.G.), Pergamon Press, Oxford, 209.

WINZLER, R.J. (1941) The respiration of bakers yeast at low oxygen tension, *J. cell. comp. Physiol.* **17**, 263—76.

WISHART, J.M. and WILKINSON, R.,(1941), Purification of settled sewage in percolating filters in series with periodic changes in the order of the filters—Results of operation of the experimental plant at Minworth, Birmingham, 1938—1940, *J. Inst. Sew. Purif.* 15—38.

WOOLDRIGE, W.R. and STANDFAST, A.F.B. (1933) The biochemical oxygen demand of sewage, *Biochem. J.* **27**, 183.

WUHRMANN, K. (1956) Factors affecting efficiency and solids production in the activated sludge process. *Biological Treatment of Sewage and IndustrialWastes* (Ed. McCABE, J. and ECKENFELDER, W.W.), Reinhold, New York, 49—65.

WUHRMANN, K. (1960) Effect of oxygen tension on biochemical reactions in sewage purification plants, *Proc. 3rd Biol. Waste Treatment Conf. Manhatten*, Paper No. 3.

# SUBJECT INDEX

(Page numbers in *italics* indicate illustrations)

# AUTHOR INDEX

*(\*Indicates included in et al reference on page indicated).*